A CLASSIC BIBLE STUDY LIBRARY

for Today

A CLASSIC BIBLE STUDY LIBRARY

for Today

Recommended by:
Charles H. Spurgeon
Warren W. Wiersbe
Cyril J. Barber
David W. Brookman
Wilbur M. Smith
Peter M. Masters
and others

KREGEL PUBLICATIONS
Grand Rapids, Michigan 49501

A Classic Bible Study Library for Today by Charles H. Spurgeon, Warren W. Wiersbe, Cyril J. Barber, David W. Brookman, Wilbur M. Smith, Peter M. Masters, et. al. © 1988, 1990 and published by Kregel Publications, a division of Kregel Inc., P. O. Box 2607, Grand Rapids, MI 49501. All rights reserved.

The publisher gratefully acknowledges the permission of all publishers listed in the Source Code List (page 79) to include quotes from their publications.

Library of Congress Cataloging-in-Publication Data

Charles H. Spurgeon, Warren W. Wiersbe, Wilbur M. Smith, Peter M. Masters, Cyril J. Barber, et. al.
A Classic Bible Study Library for Today.

Includes indexes.

1. Bible-Bibliography
I. Spurgeon, C. H. II. Title.
Z77770.C57   1988   [BS445]   016.22   88-8814

ISBN 0-8254-3762-8

3 4 5 6 Printing/Year 93 92 91 90

Printed in the United States of America

CONTENTS

Contents

PUBLISHER'S PREFACE

A Classic Bible Study Library for Today features an extensive collection of recommendations by well–known, respected church leaders. These are comments on over 280 classic books from famous past (Charles H. Spurgeon, Wilbur M. Smith, Merrill C. Tenney, etc.) and present (Warren W. Wiersbe, Cyril Barber, Peter M. Masters, J. I. Packer, etc.) church spokesmen.

These books are all published or distributed by Kregel Publications, and are "classics" because they are "works of enduring excellence" (Webster), and they persistently speak to the needs of believers, from generation to generation. Some of these great biblical studies have never been surpassed. They stand above all others for their commitment to the authority of the Scriptures and as models of theological insight and application.

Pastors, Bible students, professors, and Sunday school teachers seeking to build quality, "classic Bible study" libraries will find *A Classic Bible Study Library for Today* an excellent resource. Here is a handy listing, in biblical order, of some of the greatest biblical studies ever produced, along with comments for each title.

With the multitude of books available today, readers will find this a dependable guide to choosing those works which possess the timeless quality of commitment to the authority and proclamation of the Word of God. These classics will lead you in practical application and assist you in your teaching and preaching ministry.

The recommendations come from a diverse group of superbly qualified scholars, bibliophiles, pastors, professors and evangelists. Under each title, the source of the quote is named, and each quote is followed by a source code set in bold typeface. A quick reference to the Source Code List (p. 79) will provide more detailed information on the source of each quote.

Periodicals and individuals quoted infrequently are not listed individually in the Source Code List. Their full names are given before each quote. Individuals quoted frequently show only the last name before the quote, and detailed source information is in the Source Code List. Complete Author and Subject Indexes are included to further assist you in using this booklet.

Books are available through your local Christian bookstore. Since titles continually go out-of-print and financial considerations do not make it possible to continue reprinting all of the books, some may only be available in the second-hand market. You may want to direct your inquiries for such titles to Kregel's Bookstore, P. O. Box 2607, Grand Rapids, Michigan 49501-2607. They stock over 100,000 second-hand religious and theological books and sets.

SECTION I
BIBLE TRANSLATIONS
AND
WORKS ON THE WHOLE BIBLE

BIBLE TRANSLATIONS

THE COMPANION BIBLE

SMITH – ...has infinite value because of the remarkable series of appendixes, filling some 227 pages at the end of the volume....Material will be found in this book which is not easily available in any other volume that I know of. It is the fruit of a lifetime of exhaustive study of the Holy Scriptures. w

Rotherham, Joseph Bryant – THE EMPHASIZED BIBLE

BARBER – A literal translation of the Greek and Hebrew texts, with particular stress upon the grammatical emphasis of each verse by use of diacritical marks. ...of help...to pastors whose knowledge of Greek and Hebrew is limited. B

CUSTER – ...the ease with which the emphasized words can be spotted in a passage is a great help in perceiving where the stress in a sermon should fall for a given passage. For the pastor whose Greek and Hebrew are only a dim memory of student days, this version can bring to his mind the grammatical emphasis that only a critical knowledge of Greek and Hebrew can provide. I

LOCKYER – In its class, it is incomparable. It constitutes one of the most valuable contributions to Bible study ever conceived. N, DD

Weymouth, Richard Francis – THE NEW TESTAMENT IN MODERN SPEECH

BARBER – A most readable translation that combines a lucid style with grammatical accuracy. Old, familiar phrases take on new significance. B

BOLLIER – ...noted for its carefulness in rendering the shades of the Greek tenses. E

9

DANKER – ...noted for awareness of tenses and...displays exquisite literary taste. J

LOUIS PAUL LEHMAN – ...a treasure-house...the plethora of new translations, paraphrases, and accompanying materials, does not eliminate the need for works of proven value.... DD

MERCHANT – ...achieves a high level of accuracy.... R

COMMENTARIES AND OTHER WORKS ON THE WHOLE BIBLE

Gray, James M. – HOME BIBLE STUDY COMMENTARY

BARBER – The thoroughness and soundness of Gray's teaching continue to make this an important work for the lay church-worker. C

WIERSBE – A very fine, one-volume commentary on the entire Bible. James M. Gray was a godly man and a fine Bible student. I recommend this to keep handy on your shelf. DD

Slemming, C. W. – BIBLE DIGEST

BIBLIOTHECA SACRA – For each book [of the Bible], after a short introduction, Slemming gives a résumé of the contents of the Bible book, which presents a good overview of the book. DD

V. RAYMOND EDMAN – ...a splendid overview of the Bible. I find that a careful study of it along with the Bible is most helpful in opening up the contents of each book. DD

Williams, George – STUDENT'S COMMENTARY ON THE HOLY SCRIPTURES

BARBER – A comprehensive one-volume Bible commentary. Thoroughly conservative.... DD

HARRY BULTEMA – ...thoroughly trust-worthy for old and young, because it is fundamental in all the great doctrines, evangelical and evangelistic, premillennial and dispensational; the author is sane and pious throughout, while his style is always pungent and as clear as a bell. In this whole splendid volume, in which more truth is found than in any other volume of our day, is not found one dark sentence. DD

GRACE THEOLOGICAL JOURNAL – ...It is fresh, spiritual and inspiring. The devotional flavor is refreshing.... DD

CARL F. H. HENRY – ...holds solid evangelical views of the inspiration and authorship of the Scriptures, and of the great central doctrines. ...has provided a useful and stimulating volume. DD

Godet, Frederic L. – STUDIES IN THE OLD TESTAMENT
BARBER – ...covers a wide range of subjects including angels, the plan and development of life on earth. ...[Godet] is always worth consulting. C

Hengstenberg, E. W. – CHRISTOLOGY OF THE OLD TESTAMENT (4 vols. condensed into one)
BARBER – A first-rate study of Christ as He appears in type and prophecy in the Old Testament. Of great value to preachers. B
BROOKMAN – A complete examination of all major Messianic passages of Scripture in the Old Testament. This classic work refutes several of the radical views of liberal scholars. Excellent. G
MASTERS – ...a successful abridgement of the acclaimed (but formidable) work. The original work wasted much print repudiating dead and forgotten unbelieving scholars. This abridgement clips out most of these portions, preserving all the vital arguments of Hengstenberg as he traces the Messianic passages through the Old Testament. This...abridgement...is the most usable edition available. ...The foundation stone in the preacher's library.... P
SAMUEL J. SCHULTZ (as quoted by Merchant) – ...essential for twentieth-century theology. It is especially helpful and reliable from an evangelical perspective. For the student of the New Testament it provides an enriching background. R
SMITH – The greatest work that has ever been written on the Messianic prophecies of the Old Testament, though we do not agree with all of its interpretations. ...one of the most valuable works on prophecy ever written, filled with learning, a powerful answer to rationalism, confirming the student in his faith, and ever deepening his holy regard for the miracle of Messianic prediction.... Nothing has been written to compare with this in vastness of learning, and the firmness with which the writer sets forth his own convictions on the many disputed points of Messianic interpretation. DD, W, U

SPURGEON – This great work deals with a most vital theme in a masterly manner; it has always been held in high esteem. Y

Jones, Alfred – Dictionary of Old Testament Proper Names

CANON WORDSWORTH, Bishop of Lincoln, author of *Wordsworth's Holy Bible with notes and Introductions*, was the motivation for the preparation and writing of this work. His plan was carried out by the author. Thus we have this *Dictionary* of 3,600 Old Testament names arranged in English alphabetical order. After the English name, the Hebrew name is given, with its pronounciation. The *Septuagint* rendering, and that of the Vulgate Latin, follow. The Hebrew name is then etymologically discussed and its relations and derivations shown. DD

Thomas, W. H. Griffith – THROUGH THE PENTATEUCH: Chapter by Chapter

BARBER – Well-outlined and contains helpful thoughts on the text. B

BROOKMAN – These valuable notes take the form of a connected commentary on the Pentateuch. A helpful introduction to each book plus the excellent homiletical material will give the minister devotional insights into the Pentateuchal writings. Evangelical. G

R. K. HARRISON – ...among that elite group of authoritative expositors of God's Word in the twentieth century. A man of brilliant intellect, enormous energy, and profound Christian faith.... A lucid and uncomplicated analysis of the Pentateuch. The author's clear, crisp, straightforward style, joined as it is with wisdom, both theological and devotional, give his expository works classic status. DD

WIERSBE – Griffith Thomas excels in spiritual depth, practicality and a simplicity of expression that make the most profound truths come alive with excitement. DD

GENESIS

Alford, Henry – GENESIS AND EXODUS 1–25

BARBER – A rare work; buy it while it is available. C

BROOKMAN – [A] reprint work...by an outstanding biblical writer. G

SPURGEON – The works of this eminent scholar are too well known and appreciated to need even a word from us. Y

Bush, George – GENESIS (2 vols.)

BARBER – ...enriching comments on the text; sidelights drawn from...a thorough knowledge of the...culture. [Includes] devotional application. C

BROOKMAN – This volume contains rich expository notes based upon the original text. Of practical value to the pastor with little or no knowledge of Hebrew. G

Candlish, Robert – STUDIES IN GENESIS

BARBER – Expository messages rich in their devotional emphasis, containing helpful theological discussions. Thoroughly conservative and of special value to the pastor. ...remains one of the best works for pastors.... **B, C**

BROOKMAN – ...a very important, classic work on Genesis. It has a treasure-house of sermon suggestions and teachings. These are expository messages, thoroughly conservative, rich in devotional emphasis and contain many theological discussions that will be of special value to ministers. Doctrinal and biographical. **G**

CUSTER – A rich devotional and practical expositon. **I**

MASTERS – ...full of suggestions for preachers. One of the very few Old Testament commentaries which will help in the preparation of evangelistic addresses.... Spurgeon's favorite Genesis commentary will doubtless be the immediate favorite of many preachers today. **P**

SPURGEON – We venture to characterize this as THE work upon Genesis, so far as lectures can make up an exposition; we have greatly profited by its perusal. It should be in every biblical library. **Y**

Delitzsch, Franz J. – A NEW COMMENTARY ON GENESIS (2 vols.)

BARBER – A critical commentary on the Hebrew text that holds to the Mosaic authorship of Genesis but leaves room for final redaction in the post-exilic period. Advocates an early form of the documentary hypothesis, and holds to the "long day" theory of creation. Deserving of careful reading. **B, C**

CHILDS – ...by far the most profound commentary from a conservative theological perspective.... His penetration of theological issues and often sensitive handling of the biblical text is of a high order. **H**

DOUGLAS MOO – ...[is] separate from the Keil and Delitszch series; this is a classic theological expression. **S**

SMITH – ...in some ways the greatest commentary on Genesis in any language.... **W**

Strahan, James – HEBREW IDEALS IN GENESIS

BARBER – A rich and rewarding study. Does not permit critical considerations to mar his work. **B**

BROOKMAN – A classic reprint dealing with the heart and spirit of the people and events in Genesis. Then these Hebrew ideals are related to the ideals of life today. This is a valuable character study. **G**

SMITH – ...not as well known in this country as it deserves to be...rich blessings...are in store for the reader. ...the [devotional] classic on Genesis... [is] one of the most precious volumes on the deeper aspects of the teaching of Genesis.... **W, U, X**

ALEXANDER WHYTE (as quoted by Wilbur M. Smith) – I have read it in proof [form], and again and again since it was printed. Let that fine piece of evangelical scholarship be in every home. **x**

WIERSBE – One of my favorite books.... I think every preacher ought to have this in his library and use it faithfully. One of the most valuable studies of Genesis to appear in this century. It has enriched my life and ministry, and I am sure it will enrich yours as well. **DD**

Thomas, W. H. Griffith – GENESIS: A Devotional Commentary

ALLISON – He is able to picture the original setting of Bible events in such colorful terms that the reader feels transported to that place and time, to relive the Bible experience. **A**

BARBER – Well outlined, and contains helpful thoughts on the text. Possibly the most helpful devotional exposition of Genesis available. Pastors will find the material on Abraham, Isaac, Jacob, and Joseph to be unsurpassed. **B**

BROOKMAN – A highly recommended devotional commentary on Genesis. This author has mastered all the relevant literature pertaining to this book, making it truly sound in biblical scholarship. **G**

KAISER – ... carefully weaves the book's purpose, plan, unity, values, and doctrines into a beautiful, but challenging tapestry.... It can be used as a basis for an individual devotional on the text or as a teaching block of text.... Thomas must be commended and thanked a thousand times over for his laboring in the text in order to guide us into a realization of how that text applies to us today. For this the whole church can be grateful to our Lord. **DD**

PACKER – The author's clear, crisp, straightforward style, joined as it is with wisdom, both theological and devotional, gives his expository works classic status. **DD, Y**

ROSSCUP – This work is good in tracing the argument and showing connections between chapters. It is devotional and gives suggestions for meditation at the end of the chapters. **EE**

WIERSBE – A helpful devotional commentary. Griffith Thomas excels in spiritual depth, practicality and a simplicity of expression that make the most profound truths come alive with excitement. **BB, DD**

JOURNEYINGS OF THE CHILDREN OF ISRAEL

Ritchie, John – FROM EGYPT TO CANAAN

FAIR – ...a wealth of knowledge, excitement, and challenge await you in this small but dynamic volume. Here are rich nuggets of scriptural principles to apply to your life.... **DD, K**

THE BAPTIST BULLETIN – These studies were originally published in the late 1800's, but for the serious student of Old Testament types, they are as current as today.... New Christians who are serious about Bible study will find these helpful. They could be used for a discipleship program. DD

Wagner, George – PRACTICAL TRUTHS FROM ISRAEL'S WANDERINGS

BARBER – A welcome reprint. C

BROOKMAN – The author draws out similarities between Israel's wanderings in the wilderness and a Christian's pilgrimage through life. A classic reprint of 384 pages. G

SPURGEON – A book which we have read with great pleasure and profit, and very heartily recommend. Y

WIERSBE – [Contains] rich veins of gold that others have ignored or neglected. I rejoice that [this] classic is available again for people who are serious about Bible study. ...you [will] find insights from the Scriptures that can enrich your life and ministry.... DD

THE TABERNACLE

Kurtz, John Henry – THE SACRIFICIAL WORSHIP OF THE OLD TESTAMENT

BARBER – Thoroughly conservative and evangelical, Kurtz's treatment even today makes rewarding reading and serves as an effective counter-balance to other more liberal works whose viewpoints continue to recur in modern discussions. B

Ritchie, John – THE TABERNACLE IN THE WILDERNESS

FAIR – ...practical, simply-stated truths, yet deeply enriching.... What a thrilling parallel between the Old Testament tabernacle and a Christian's life is given here! DD, K

Soltau, Henry W. – THE HOLY VESSELS AND FURNITURE OF THE TABERNACLE

BARBER – ...designed to give a correct exposition of the texts relating to the Tabernacle and its furniture, and to present the typical teaching with regard to Christ and His work. B

BROOKMAN – Very helpful exposition giving the most correct delineation from Scripture of the contents of the Tabernacle that has ever appeared. The furniture and vessels used in the Tabernacle are all treated in their typical significance for the believer's instruction, and the riches of the Old Testament economy are unfolded for the New Testament saint. G

MASTERS – This famous old work has ten color plates with devotional comments and some lessons drawn. B

SPURGEON – A series of sumptuous pictures, executed in the best style of art, impressing the mind far more vividly than any letter-press could do. Y

WIERSBE – ...an excellent volume. BB

Soltau, Henry W. – THE TABERNACLE, THE PRIESTHOOD, AND THE OFFERINGS

BARBER – A classic study sufficiently detailed to be helpful. Avoids typology and fanciful spiritualization, and expounds the Scripture with reverence and clarity. B

BROOKMAN – A classic, comprehensive study unfolding the beauties and glories of the Lord Jesus Christ as portrayed in the Jewish ritual. This work avoids extreme and fanciful spiritualization often found in many books on typology. Contains a wealth of direct, practical teaching regarding the daily life of the Christian and the maintenance of communion with God. G

MASTERS – ...packed with information and suggested practical application. Worth any commentary on Exodus and Leviticus. Extremely readable and a very good value. O

SPURGEON – Richly suggestive. Exceedingly well worked out in details; but not so wire-drawn as to prevent thought on the reader's part. Y

WIERSBE – ...an excellent volume. BB

LEVITICUS

Kellogg, Samuel H. – STUDIES IN LEVITICUS

ALLISON – Kellogg gives more emphasis to the historical impact that Jewish civil laws had upon their worship. A

BARBER – Perhaps the finest exposition of this portion of God's Word ever to come from the pen of man. An exemplary study.... Should be in every pastor's library. B, C

BROOKMAN – An outstanding commentary on Leviticus.... In this work, Kellogg staunchly defends Mosaic authorship and ably treats Jewish ceremonial law in all its aspects. G

DOUGLAS MOO – Magnificent old classic. Readable, well-studied, evangelical, and quite helpful for the pastor. S

SAMUEL J. SCHULTZ (as quoted by Merchant) – A very helpful commentary, providing helpful insight and understanding concerning the details of the religion of Israel.... R

WIERSBE – ...a classic. DD

DEUTERONOMY

Cumming, John – THE BOOK OF DEUTERONOMY

BARBER – Of special value due to the fact that there are so few homiletical studies of Deuteronomy. ...a series of "homely" expositions for general readers. Old-fashioned, but lively (almost conversational) and furnishing

a constant flow of spiritual applications. ...abounds in warmly
evangelical, personal lessons. B, C
BROOKMAN – ...the best-known of Dr. Cumming's more than 200
expositions of many of the books of the Bible. It is a classic...containing
homely expositions rather than a verse-by-verse commentary. G
SPURGEON – Pretty, popular, profitable. Y

HISTORICAL BOOKS

Meyer, F. B. – CHOICE NOTES ON JOSHUA—2 KINGS

FAIR – ...very clear.....plain, practical, precise, perceptive and
profitable.... K, DD
BROOKMAN – The design of this book is to make understandable [and]
accessible notes from the books of Joshua to Second Kings. This work
will bring new understanding, insight and challenge. A chapter-by-
chapter study. Devotional. G

JUDGES
SEE ALSO "HISTORICAL BOOKS"

Wiseman, Luke H. – PRACTICAL TRUTHS FROM JUDGES

BARBER – ...contains a wealth of practical material; applications are offered
to encourage and challenge us today. C
BROOKMAN – A valuable classic reprint study that presents a general
overview of the period of the Judges along with an in-depth study of
the lives of Barak, Gideon, Jephtah, and Samson. The author shows
extensive research.... G
SPURGEON – Mr. Wiseman in this work tells "of Gideon and Barak, of
Samson and of Jephthah," and he does it in a powerful style. He was
one of the best preachers in the Wesleyan body. A man of fullness, and
judiciousness; in fact, a wise man. Y
WIERSBE – [Contains] rich veins of gold that others have ignored or
neglected. I rejoice that [this] classic is available again for people who
are serious about Bible study. ...you [will] find insights from the
Scriptures that can enrich your life and ministry.... DD

PSALMS

Clarke, Arthur G. – ANALYTICAL STUDIES IN THE PSALMS

BARBER – Prefaced with a comprehensive introduction to the Psalms,
their nature, scope, and use in Israel's worship. Complete with outlines
based on the Hebrew text, notes on the text, and exegetical comments.

...exceedingly helpful for preachers. ...these brief analyses of each Psalm breathe the confidence of one whose reliance was established on the unchanging character of God. c, DD

BROOKMAN – An excellent treatment of the Book of Psalms, featuring homiletical outlines and practical applications. This classic study...presents an analysis of each Psalm and its relationship to the canon of Scripture. G

W. E. VINE – ...a comprehensive and useful volume. It affords [me] a very great pleasure to commend this work to servants of God. DD

WIERSBE – I only wish I had known about this book earlier in my ministry.... I know of no other book, apart from Scroggie's on Psalms, which unlocks the meanings found in the Psalms. [Clarke] accomplishes this feat with excellent results. DD

Dickson, David – COMMENTARY ON THE PSALMS (2 vols.)

BARBER – A richly devotional exposition by a Scottish Covenanter of the seventeenth century...exhibit[s] a vibrancy of faith and a care in exposition that is refreshing. B, C

CHILDS – The exegesis is warm, vigorous, bold, and devotional...is highly recommended. H

GRIER – Spurgeon termed this "a rich volume, dropping fatness." L

MASTERS – ...filled with deep reflections, doctrinal observations and applications to the spiritual life. Very important...highly stimulating to preachers. P

SPURGEON – Invaluable to the preacher. Having read and re-read it, we can speak of its holy savor and suggestiveness. We commend it with much fervor. Y

WIERSBE – ...will rejoice your soul. BB

Meyer, F. B. – CHOICE NOTES ON THE PSALMS

FAIR – ...a classic in its brevity and beauty of clarity. [It] will give delight and blessed learning. Meyer is pastorally at his best in this brief commentary. K, DD

Meyer, F. B. – THE SHEPHERD PSALM

BARBER – A warmly devotional exposition. B

BROOKMAN – Meyer has put together a warmly devotional exposition on Psalm Twenty-three. This work will aid the minister that attempts to do a series of messages on this important Psalm of the Old Testament. G

PHILLIP KELLER – This...book, if read with an open and receptive spirit, will enrich the reader's life. Read...and rejoice in its green pastures. DD

Perowne, J. J. Stewart – COMMENTARY ON THE PSALMS (2 Vols. in 1)

BAPTIST STANDARD – ...With each psalm, Perowne gives an extensive introduction, including its theology; follows with a translation and commentary, always aware of the messianic hope therein; and closes with a detailed analysis of Hebrew words. This is a rich and inspiring study. DD

BARBER – Contains valuable exegetical studies....The introductory essays...make [for] rewarding reading. B

BROOKMAN – Perowne provides a complete background on each Psalm and clear-cut concise marginal notes that give the reader "at-a-glance" information. Reformed. G

CHILDS – My first choice among older English commentaries....[Perowne] has a good knowledge of the history of exegesis and a profound sense of the unity of the two Testaments. H

CHRISTIAN RETAILING – ...Perowne brings new insight into the Psalter's implications and shows how even the placement of the word in the Hebrew language had significance above and beyond the actual words used. DD

WALTER C. KAISER, JR. – Perowne is able to do what some of the moderns with all their new insights are unable to do since they often do not approach the text with the same reverential humility or with the same regard for the author's truth-intention. DD

MOO – A classic commentary on the Hebrew text of the Psalms....Has long been an evangelical standard. S

ROSSCUP – Distinguished among 19th century works on Psalms...is detailed and discerning along evangelical lines....[Perowne] shows, among other things, that the psalmist often went far beyond himself in statements and projected his thought prophetically to Christ. In most cases the verse by verse commentary solidly explains the text....often shows the unity between a Psalms statement and New Testament truth. EE

Smith, George Adam – FOUR PSALMS

F. F. BRUCE – ...it illustrates the gifts of linguistic and geographical knowledge and religious insight which [Smith] brought to the exposition of Scripture. Its reappearance is...welcome. DD

Spurgeon, C. H. – THE TREASURY OF DAVID (*Psalms* abridged by David Otis Fuller)

BARBER – A classic in its field. Richly rewarding, deeply devotional, and pleasingly relevant. Provides not only the thoughts of the great "Prince of Preachers" of the last century, but also an abundance of quotations taken from the writings of those who have preceded him in the ministry of the Word. B

GRIER – Preachers and teachers will find much useful material [here].... L

ROBERT G. LEE – Reading this condensation, one has the joy of a diver who, "standing naked for the plunge, rejoices when he comes up with hands filled with pearls." [Contains] the wealth of the spiritual riches of God's truth and the wonder of God's gospel.... This condensation...brings us the assembled sweetness of many fields into one garden of rare and radiant blossoms and fruitage. DD

LOCKYER – ...a success.... The selection...in no way detracts from Spurgeon's original work. N, DD

MASTERS – ...a one-volume edited and abridged edition of *The Treasury of David*...for those who would like the Treasury in shortened form for the purpose of, say, private devotions, this is an ideal size and a very fine piece of work. B

ROSSCUP – In this most detailed exposition, the London pulpit master deals with each verse with a wealth of illustration, practical comment, and preaching hints....On any given verse one can expect to find exposition or quotes looking at it from various angles. The devotional flavor is excellent. Here is a suggestive source for preacher or teacher and much wealth for general readers....The condensation is a help to the busy who want to get at the hub of things quickly. EE

PROVERBS

Arnot, William – STUDIES IN PROVERBS

BARBER – Perceptive studies of selected verses in the Book of Proverbs. [They] provide both practical instruction and spiritual direction. B, C

BROOKMAN – The author's aim was to be doctrinal, spiritual and practical. A classic work. G

MASTERS – A fine companion for daily Bible study, with some good points to stimulate preachers also. P

ROSSCUP – ...The 583 page work is famous for the grasp of spiritual truths and the easy-flowing style. EE

SPURGEON – We wish Dr. Arnot had gone steadily through the whole book, for his mind was of an order peculiarly adapted for such a task. Those passages which he dilates upon are set in a clear and beautiful light. For a happy blending of illustrative faculty, practical sound sense, and spirituality, Dr. Arnot was almost unrivalled. Y

WIERSBE – ...a gold mine of spiritual truth. BB

Lawson, George – EXPOSITION OF PROVERBS

BARBER – ...rich, rewarding insights...in this able Scot's warm devotional exposition. DD

BROOKMAN – This practical classic on Proverbs will bring a source of spiritual strength, wisdom and direction for every minister and Bible student of the Word of God. Devotional. G

MASTERS – This practical treatment...has a charm of its own. P

ROSSCUP – ...This has to rate as one of the most helpful older works in reference to the main task of explaining the sense of verses, usually quite well. EE

SPURGEON – A thoroughly sound and useful commentary. Lawson wrote popularly and vigorously. Y

SONG OF SOLOMON

Durham, James – EXPOSITION OF THE SONG OF SOLOMON

BROOKMAN – Durham understands the Song of Solomon as an allegory of the relationship between Christ and the believer. G

SPURGEON – Durham is always good, and he is at his best upon the Canticles. Y

JEREMIAH

von Orelli, Hans Conrad – THE PROPHECIES OF JEREMIAH

BARBER – A moderately conservative, exegetical and expository work. B

EZEKIEL

Fairbairn, Patrick – COMMENTARY ON EZEKIEL

BROOKMAN – ...valuable expository study. Fairbairn ably handles some difficult passages of Scripture from the book of Ezekiel. GG

MASTERS – Fairbairn's masterly interpretive descriptions will prove of incalculable help....This commentary will certainly help the user to recognize the many parallels between the themes of the ancient church and our activities today. DD

Moo – A thorough, yet easy-to-read work. Well researched and the best evangelical book available on Ezekiel. S

ROSSCUP – This amillennial work is quite old but shows the student how a man of that persuasion dealt with the great prophetical portions like chapters 34-48. EE

SPURGEON – This exposition...has gained for its author a high place among elucidators of difficult parts of Scripture. DD

DANIEL

Anderson, Sir Robert – THE COMING PRINCE

BARBER – Focuses upon Daniel's prophecy of the seventy weeks, and traces its chronological development through to the time when Messiah was "cut off" at the end of the sixty-ninth week. Provides reconstruction of the chronology, and deals with the times of the Gentiles, the tribulation period, and the Second Advent of Christ. B

BROOKMAN – One of the most detailed works ever written on Daniel's Seventieth Week and the coming Antichrist. G

WIERSBE – ...an excellent study. BB

Gaebelein, Arno C. – THE PROPHET DANIEL

ALLISON – ...one of the leading premillennial, dispensational works on Daniel. A

BARBER – A chapter-by-chapter treatment of the visions and prophecies of Daniel which presents the essence of the predictive ministry of the prophet and expounds the prophecy in an enlighting and helpful way from the premillennial perspective. DD

ROSSCUP – Dividing the book of Daniel according to the languages in the original text, the writer gives a brief yet helpful survey of a dispensational interpretation. EE

Pusey, Edward B. – DANIEL, THE PROPHET

BARBER – An extensive, scholarly treatment. Ably defends the authorship and integrity of Daniel's prophecy. Amillennial. B

BROOKMAN – ...a classic conservative work. G

SPURGEON – To Dr. Pusey's work on Daniel all subsequent writers must be deeply indebted, however much they may differ from him in other departments of theological study. Y

THE MINOR PROPHETS

von Orelli, Hans Conrad – THE TWELVE MINOR PROPHETS

ALLISON – ...gives us a real treasure of Hebrew word studies. Von Orelli was widely respected as a knowledgeable conservative scholar of Semitics. His footnotes are rich with insights into the Old Testament text. A

BARBER – A most valuable study by a moderately conservative German theologian. B

BROOKMAN – The meanings of Hebrew words are brought to light by a simple but full English explanation. This classic work is based upon sound scholarship. Conservative. G

MOO – A very usable and easy-to-read work. Thoroughly researched and evangelical....S

AMOS

Cripps, Richard S. – COMMENTARY ON AMOS

ALLISON – ...his practical comments on the text are helpful. A

BARBER – Not abreast of the latest archaeological material. The exposition, however, is very full...deserving of close study. B, C

BROOKMAN – This full exposition contains many practical applications to the needs of today. Conservative. G

OBADIAH

Marbury, Edward – OBADIAH AND HABAKKUK

BROOKMAN – Marbury's work on Obadiah and Habakkuk is a true classic.... This work will be of great benefit to every minister and Bible student. G

SPURGEON – Far more lively than Rainolds. His spirituality of mind prevents his learning becoming dull. He says in the preface, "All my desire is to do all the good I can," and he writes in that spirit. Y

JONAH

Burn, Samuel C. – THE PROPHET JONAH

BARBER – All things considered, this is one of the best expositions on this Old Testament book for the preacher. C

BROOKMAN – Every minister will be able to glean some homiletical treasures from this practical work. G

Exell, Joseph S. – PRACTICAL TRUTHS FROM JONAH

BARBER – A capable devotional commentary...based on sound scholarship. C

BROOKMAN – This verse-by-verse exposition deals with the practical aspects of the Book of Jonah. Exell was an excellent devotional writer. Conservative. G

MASTERS – ...exactly what its title claims, and worthily adds to the fine treatments which Jonah has attracted. B

SPURGEON – Mr. Exell, in a very unpretending but able way, brings to light the practical lessons of Jonah. Paxton Hood calls these readings "admirable," and we concur in the verdict. Y

WIERSBE – [Contains] rich veins of gold that others have ignored or neglected. I rejoice that [this] classic is available again for people who are serious about Bible study. ...you [will] find insights from the Scriptures that can enrich your life and ministry.... DD

Kirk, Thomas – JONAH: HIS LIFE AND MISSION

BARBER – It is difficult to think of any devout Bible student failing to receive blessing from a perusal of this fine work. C

BROOKMAN – ...expository, fresh, and suggestive. Kirk has an intriguing way of making Bible characters come alive. Conservative. G

HABAKKUK

Marbury, Edward – OBADIAH AND HABAKKUK

BROOKMAN – Marbury's work on Obadiah and Habakkuk is a true classic.... This work will be of great benefit to every minister and Bible student. G

SPURGEON – Here Marbury holds the field alone among old English authors, and he does so worthily. There is about him a vigorous, earnest freshness which makes his pages glow. Y

ZECHARIAH

Baron, David – COMMENTARY ON ZECHARIAH: His Visions and Prophecies

BARBER – ...a helpful elucidation of the messianic prophecies contained in this book. B

BROOKMAN – ...one of the best commentaries on Zechariah. G

CUSTER – ...thorough premillennial exegesis by a Hebrew-Christian, who knows both the language and the customs of his people. The work is warmly devotional and gives a clear portrait of Israel's place in God's prophetic program. I

WALTER C. KAISER, JR. – One of Baron's crowning achievements....Baron has given us a rich treat of theology and exegesis in this study. Few...are as adept as he is in tracing the inner connections between the sections of this prophecy and its organic unity, logic, and thrust.... It would appear that he literally lived with this Scripture.... By any fair standards of comparison, this work is still one of the monumental statements of all time on the meaning and significance of Zechariah. DD

SMITH – In some ways I believe this is the greatest volume devoted entirely to the exposition of any one of the Minor Prophets in our language. When one has Baron's work he needs little else on Zechariah...not only a work of great scholarship, but one that is exceptionally rich devotionally, warm with spiritual teachings, so that the entire volume not only illuminates the mind, but enriches the soul.... Indeed, here is a volume that should be in every Bible student's library, one not as well-known as it ought to be, but of the very first importance in understanding this portion of the prophetic Scriptures.... W, X

WIERSBE – A recognized Hebrew-Christian scholar whose commentary is *the* commentary on this book. It is hard to find a good commentary on Zechariah. David Baron has given us one of the best. BB, DD

Wright, Charles H. – ZECHARIAH AND HIS PROPHECIES

BARBER – ...these extensive studies translate, introduce, and treat the visions of this neglected Old Testament prophet. Amillennial. C

BROOKMAN – Dr. Wright's exposition is both scholarly and conservative. G

SECTION III
NEW TESTAMENT

Barnes, Albert – BARNES' NOTES ON THE NEW TESTAMENT

MASTERS – As the publishers state, every word of Barnes is included. This is a beautiful production and frankly makes nonsense of the multi–volume edition. His "Notes" are full of information, and he summarizes the views of all the key expositors up to his time. Regular users grow very attached to these notes, which are especially valuable to preachers. Dr. Barnes had particular skill when it came to summarizing opposing views on controversial passages . For these problem passages he has a clarity generally unmatched by others. P, Q

SPURGEON – Everybody has this work, and therefore can judge for himself, or we would both commend and criticize. Y

WIERSBE – ...a detailed commentary...most satisfactory. DD

Bengel, John Albert – NEW TESTAMENT COMMENTARY

(2 vols.) (Original title: *The Gnomon of the New Testament*)

BARBER – ...contains valuable insights into the Greek of the New Testament and is still sought after...[it] is worthy of repeated consultation. B, C

DANKER – ...anticipates and influences considerably both German and English scholarship of the next century and combines perspicuity with brevity in a most remarkable manner. In a single line of Bengel's comment there is frequently more spiritual freight than garrulous predecessors and contemporaries packed into a page. *Gnomon* is the Latin term, now adopted into English, for the pin, or style of a sundial. Bengel's comments are just that: his style points the student directly to the timely meaning of the text and is not simply the dress of thought, tailored to fit some fixed fashion.... J

A. T. ROBERTSON – ...one of the great commentaries of the New Testament for scholarly and spiritual insight. DD

PHILIP SCHAFF – A marvel of condensation and spiritual insight; must remain a classic. DD

SPURGEON – ...the scholar's delight. He selected the title *Gnomon* as modest and appropriate, intending it in the sense of a pointer or indicator, like the sundial; his aim being to point out or indicate the full force and meaning of the words and sentences of the New Testament. He endeavors to let the text itself cast its shadow on his page, believing with Luther that "the science of theology is nothing else but grammar exercised on the words of the Holy Spirit." The editor...says in his preface: "It is quite superfluous to write in praise of the *Gnomon* of Bengel. Though modern criticism has furnished many valuable additions to our materials for New Testament exegesis, yet, in some respects, Bengel stands out still...among all who have labored, or who as yet labor in that important field. He is unrivaled in felicitous brevity, combined with what seldom accompanies that excellence, namely, perspicuity. Terse, weighty, and suggestive, he often, as a modern writer observes, 'condenses more matter into a line, than can be extracted from pages of other writers'." ...the pioneer of true biblical criticism. Y

MARVIN R. VINCENT – [Bengel] must always stand preeminent for his keen and deep spiritual insight and for that marvelously terse and pithy diction with which, as a master key, he so often throws open by a single turn, the secret chambers of a word. DD

WIERSBE – One of the sets I use often in my library...a fine book.... Old, yes, but filled with good treasures for the careful student of the Word of God. DD

Fairweather, William – BACKGROUND OF THE GOSPELS

BARBER – A very important older work tracing the historical and doctrinal themes of the intertestamental period and the preparation of the Greco-Roman world for the coming of Christ. Provides all that the busy pastor could desire. An indispensable work. Will handsomely repay the busy pastor each time he uses it. B, C

BROOKMAN – Fairweather...traces historically and religiously the interval beginning with the Maccabean revolt and ending with the destruction of Jerusalem. G

Godet, Frederic L. – STUDIES IN THE NEW TESTAMENT

BARBER – ...these studies cover differences in the four Gospels, the person and work of Christ, the leading apostles, and the structure of the Book of Revelation. C

Hort, F. J. & Hort, A. F. – EXPOSITORY AND EXEGETICAL STUDIES (Includes: *Prolegomena to Romans and Ephesians,*

*Epistle of St. James, First Epistle of St. Peter, The Apocalypse of
St. John 1 3* and *The Gospel According to St. Mark.*)
BARBER – ...the reissuing of all of [Hort's] works in one handy volume is
extremely fortuitous. c

Zahn, Theodor – INTRODUCTION TO THE NEW TESTAMENT (3 vols.)
BARBER – ...Zahn's work is...extensive and contains a mine of valuable
material. It should be consulted by all students of the New Testament. c
CUSTER – The...classic in the field.... i
DANKER – ...impressive for its profound learning. j
SMITH – ...without doubt the greatest New Testament scholar in the
world during the latter part of the 19th century, and a thorough
conservative. His work is the most important of its kind ever to be
published, and if a Bible student really wants to master the difficult but
important problems relating to the literature of the New Testament, this
is the one volume to study. w

LIFE OF JESUS CHRIST
SEE ALSO "CHRISTOLOGY"

Arnot, William – LESSER PARABLES OF OUR LORD
BARBER – A valuable resource...in spite of its vintage. B, C
BROOKMAN – ...a classic on the lesser-known parables. One will discover
varied theological and biblical concepts embedded in these parables. G

Fraser, Donald – THE METAPHORS OF CHRIST
BARBER – A must for all who desire to know how Christ used metaphors
to communicate truth to His hearers. This study may well serve as a
model of good communication even today. Excellent. c

Habershon, Ada R. – STUDY OF THE PARABLES
BARBER – A perceptive treatment by a capable Hebrew-Christian writer. B
SMITH – I do not know of any work on the parables which brings forth so
much new, fresh, suggestive and often profound truth as the volume by
Miss Habershon. She was one of the deepest Bible students and clearest
writers on biblical subjects of her day.... w

Innes, Alexander T. & Powell, Frank J. – THE TRIAL OF CHRIST (2 vols. in one)
BARBER – Two British [lawyers] examine the trials of Jesus Christ from
different...points of view. The result is a pair of legal monographs that
are deserving of a place in every zealous Christian's library. Highly
recommended. c

BROOKMAN – An excellent combination of two works that trace the order of events of Christ's trials and death. G

Liddon, Henry P. – THE DIVINITY OF OUR LORD

BARBER – ...a standard treatment on the subject for more than a century...the information presented is of such a nature that it strengthens the reader's faith and also grounds his belief in the "impregnable rock of Holy Scripture." Excellent. Preachers will have call to refer to this book often. B, C

BROOKMAN – A classic reprint on the Divinity of Christ. G

GRIER – Still valuable, though delivered over a century ago. L

C. W. GROGAN (as quoted by Merchant) – ...a great classic on the subject.... The wedding of scholarship and devotion in it makes it heartwarming as well as instructive. R

SMITH – This monumental, scholarly work is undoubtedly the greatest treatment by any one author of the preeminently important subject of the deity of our Lord Jesus Christ that was ever written in the English language.... The truths here touched upon are presented in a noble style, every page revealing a profound acquaintance with all relevant literature. A minister really commits a professional sin when he permits literature of an ephemeral and secondary nature to absorb the precious hours of his mornings, when such a great work as this stands before him pleading for a close study, with the promise that his whole life will thereby be enriched, and his convictions concerning the Lord Jesus Christ deepened, strengthened, and broadened. W

Liddon, H. P. & Orr, James – THE BIRTH OF CHRIST (*The Magnificat* and *The Virgin Birth of Christ*, 2 vols. in one)

SMITH – The Magnificat is treated exhaustively in a series of four sermons....U

SMITH – The Virgin Birth...includes a valuable appendix of papers on the subject by such biblical scholars as Wm. Sanday, Sir William Ramsay, H. Bavinck, Bishop Moule, etc. U

Maclaren, Alexander & Swete, Henry B. – THE POST-RESURRECTION MINSTRY OF CHRIST (*After the Resurrection* and *The Appearances of Our Lord After the Passion*, 2 vols. in one)

BARBER – ...deserving of careful consideration. They have been described as "brilliant and effective," evidencing "mastery of the subject matter," and being representative of the finest scholarly and suggestive material ever written on this long-neglected aspect of Christ's ministry. C

BROOKMAN – An excellent combination on the post-resurrection appearances of Christ by two outstanding authors. These two books have been uniquely blended together to form a valuable study on this subject. G

Marsh, F. E. – WHY DID CHRIST DIE?

BARBER – A Christ-centered, scriptural exposition of the atonement. B
BROOKMAN – A sound exposition of the various practical and theological aspects of the atonement. Four common errors regarding the atonement are examined carefully. This work has some excellent homiletical values. G

McIntosh, Hugh – IS CHRIST INFALLIBLE AND THE BIBLE TRUE?

BARBER – This work has long been buried in oblivion because the author dared to expose (through their own writings!) some of the leading scholars of his day: George Adam Smith, William Robertson Smith, John Watson, et al. Nor does he hesitate to take on the different European schools of thought whose views, in modified form, still are being taught today. What remains is a powerful, well-reasoned apologetic for a belief in the inspiration and inerrancy of Scripture. B

Milligan, William – THE ASCENSION OF CHRIST

BARBER – Combines excellence in presentation with accuracy in interpretation to make this study of Christ's post-resurrection and present heavenly ministries a book that all Christians will enjoy reading. C

Morgan, G. Campbell – THE CRISES OF THE CHRIST

BAPTIST EXAMINER – ...gives a very full, clear, detailed, rich, and practical exposition. DD
BAPTIST STANDARD – ...brings forth perhaps his most profound literary accomplishment in this study of the seven most impressive events in Christ's life. DD
BARBER – A timely series of studies. Should be read at frequent intervals. B
BEREA BAPTIST BANNER – A unique examination of Christ's person and work as seen through the seven climatic events of His life–His incarnation, baptism, temptation, transfiguration, crucifixion, resurrection, and ascension. DD
BROOKMAN – A practical examination of the life of Christ as the accomplishment of a Divine work. Excellent. G
GROGAN – ...the author's greatest book....shows how [Christ] meets man's many-sided need. R
PULPIT HELPS – It is Christology at its apex, and represents perhaps the best the human mind can do, to understand and explain the redemptive mysteries of the Incarnation....As one reads its pages, he repeatedly feels like sinking to his knees in praise and adoration. DD
ROSSCUP – A study of the Incarnation, the Baptism, the Temptation, the Transfiguration, the Crucifixion, the Resurrection and the Ascension. Morgan's insight into these events is penetrating, stimulating, and suggestive for teaching or sermonic material as well as devotionally enriching. EE
SMITH – ...The most important single volume that Dr. Morgan ever wrote.

It is a matsterpiece. No one volume has ever had as much influence over my thinking in my conception of the Lord Jesus Christ as this work. This is one of those books that a minister should secure on the very threshold of his life work. w

Moule, H. C. G. & Orr, James – THE RESURRECTION OF CHRIST (*Jesus and the Resurrection* and *The Resurrection of Jesus,* 2 vols. in one)

BARBER – ...provides pastors and students with a rare combination of excellence in exposition coupled with a clear enunciation of theological truth. c

Ramsay, William H. – THE EDUCATION OF CHRIST

BARBER – An informative, historical study that makes a unique contribution to our knowledge of the time. B

EDWARD M. BLAIKLOCK – Its pages will serve as an introduction to the man, and his insight into that strong interweaving of place and time, of stage and circumstance, which were part of his [Ramsay's] contribution to ancient studies. They may never be separated again. DD

Schilder, Klass – CHRIST ON TRIAL

BARBER – Covers the events of the night of His betrayal to His condemnation. A learned, accurate treatment. B

BROOKMAN – This classic work covers the events of the night of Christ's betrayal to His actual condemnation. c

Schilder, Klass – CHRIST IN HIS SUFFERING

BARBER – A classic treatment on the passion of Christ. Deserves a place in every pastor's library. B

BROOKMAN – This classic work deals with Christ's distress during the beginning stages and ends with Gethsemane. G

Schilder, Klass – CHRIST CRUCIFIED

BARBER – Theologically accurate, abounds in suggestive insights, and provides exegetical illumination for a score of Easter sermons. B

BROOKMAN – Schilder's works on the life of Christ are loaded with sermon material. This study on the crucifixion of Christ is a classic. G

Stier, Rudolf E. – THE WORDS OF THE RISEN CHRIST

BARBER – An extensive study revealing the author's mystical leanings, thorough familiarity with ascetic literature, and unique ability to present Greek concepts and word studies in a pleasing manner. Abounds in suggestive material for a series of sermons. B, c

Thomas, W. H. Griffith – CHRISTIANITY IS CHRIST

BARBER – Centers on the person and work of Christ, vindicates the uniqueness of His character and mission, establishes the credibility of

the gospel records, and deals convincingly with the meaning of and need for His bodily resurrection. A most important volume. **B**
BROOKMAN – ...[a] good older work. **G**
CHARLES C. RYRIE – It is concise yet complete. It is simple yet thorough. It is straightforward and sobering. It is faithful to the Bible. ...Altogether it is a fine apologetic for the Christian faith. **DD**

MATTHEW

Broadus, John A. – COMMENTARY ON MATTHEW

BARBER – ...a helpful exposition based upon careful exegesis and containing practical applications of the text that will be of help to preachers. **B**

BROOKMAN – This work contains a detailed introduction, expositions, and a wealth of homiletical and practical notes. **G**

MOO – ...one of the best....Broadus is packed with good things for the pastor....his exegesis and exposition are accurate, warm-hearted, and provocative. **S**

ROSSCUP – In many ways this is the finest and most satisfying overall commentary on Matthew....Broadus deals frontally with problems and gives much rich material that throws light on the text. His citations from other sources are often very helpful. **EE**

SMITH – On Matthew, the greatest work of a former generation, and still valuable. **W**

WIERSBE – Broadus' commentary has survived the test of time while other volumes have been forgotten. Broadus was a careful scholar and a great teacher of preachers. **BB**

Morison, James – THE GOSPEL OF MATTHEW

BARBER – A practical and devotional, phrase-by-phrase commentary. In many instances, provides helpful comments on textual problems. **B**

BROOKMAN – ...Morrison was an outstanding expository preacher who influenced the spiritual awakening in several parts of Scotland in the 1800's. [An] excellent devotional, phrase-by-phrase commentary.... **G**

SPURGEON – We differ greatly in doctrinal views from Dr. Morison, but we set a great price upon his Matthew and Mark, which deserve the utmost praise. **Y**

Powell, Ivor – MATTHEW'S MAJESTIC GOSPEL

AUSTRALIAN EVANGELICAL – The first Gospel dissected, chapter by chapter, with alliterative outlines and stimulating interpretive comments. **DD**

BIBLICAL EVANGELIST – ...How does one sum up Powell's works? Fresh, different, delightful are three adjectives that quickly come to mind. Any money invested in his books will not be wasted. **DD**

WIERSBE – Don't overlook this fine book. It is filled with treasures of sermon ideas and spiritual truths to help you in your ministry. **DD**

Thomas, W. H. Griffith – OUTLINE STUDIES IN MATTHEW

BARBER – This work contains nearly 500 pages of homiletical and expository outlines. B

DONALD K. CAMPBELL – ...sound interpretation and practical application of truth.... Those who preach and/or teach the Bible will be helped by these studies, as they observe the method of a biblical scholar who possessed a rare, homiletical gift. DD

PACKER – The author's clear, crisp, straightforward style, joined as it is with wisdom, both theological and devotional, gives his expository works classic status. DD, Y

ROSSCUP – ...very well-outlined, concise work.... The crisp, quick-moving lay-out of points makes this a good survey and a catalyst for a teacher of a Bible class of laymen. The work is dispensational in its perspective and even pre-tribulational as to the rapture. The author was unusually well-organized and knowledgeable as to pertinent biblical details and their correlation.... EE

WIERSBE – ...shows...his scholarship, devotion to Christ, and ability to analyze and outline Scripture. Griffith Thomas excels in spiritual depth, practicality and a simplicity of expression that make the most profound truths come alive with excitement. BB, DD

MARK

Alexander, Joseph Addison – COMMENTARY ON MARK

BROOKMAN – This classic reprint is one of the best older works on the Gospel of Mark. Alexander gives a good defense of Mark as an independent witness to the life of Christ. G

GRIER – A helpful exposition. L

MASTERS – ...provides the most lucid commentary available...a fine commentary. P, Q

SPURGEON – Alexander expounds Mark as an independent record, and does not constantly tell us to "see Matthew and Luke." Hence the book is complete in itself, and the author's learning and care have made it invaluable. Y

Morison, James – THE GOSPEL OF MARK

BARBER – A very full, devotional treatment. The overall strength of this exposition far outweighs its syntactical deficiencies. ...a commentary all expositors and students of the Word will want to own. Buy it! B, C

BROOKMAN – ...devotional. ...a companion volume to Morison's commentary on Matthew. G

SPURGEON – A deeply learned work; we know of none more thorough. Differing as we do from this author's theology, we nevertheless set a high price upon this production. Y

Powell, Ivor – MARK'S SUPERB GOSPEL

BAPTIST EXAMINER – One will be intrigued, blessed, and helped by the outline studies of chapters and sections of this book. DD

BAPTIST EXAMINER – ...The book comes alive in one's hand as he reads this commentary. The book is of great homiletic value; more than most, even good commentaries. DD

BAPTIST STANDARD – ...combines expository notes and special homilies with almost every verse or scripture passage to better aid pastors for preparing sermons, teachers for Bible class lessons and students for spiritual growth. DD

BIBLICAL EVANGELIST – This commentary is a preacher's dream! And we hasten to add that if Sunday school teachers are looking for material on the Gospel of Mark, they will not be disappointed either....covers every verse and is beautifully outlined, a matter which preachers and teachers will especially appreciate. In addition to the expository comments and outlines within the text, there are also 19 different homilies scattered throughout. DD

WIERSBE – Don't overlook this fine book.... It is filled with treasures of sermon ideas and spiritual truths to help you in your ministry. DD

Swete, H. B. – COMMENTARY ON MARK

ALLISON – Reviewers recommend this more than any other commentary on Mark.... Be sure to consult this classic.... A

BARBER – Long regarded as one of the finest exegetical treatments available. B, C

CUSTER – The most thorough commentary on the Greek text of Mark. I

ROSSCUP – ...one of the best older conservative commentaries on the Greek text. Swete was an Anglican minister and a scholar in Latin, Greek, and theology. EE

SMITH – For one who is able to follow the Greek text, this volume will be found to be one of the richest commentaries on any New Testament book ever published in our language. It is simply packed with a wealth of material, with exhaustive analyses, and fine, accurate, compact definitions. W

TENNEY (as quoted by Merchant) – A commentary of solid worth.... R, AA

WIERSBE – ...a scholarly commentary you should buy. BB

LUKE

Powell, Ivor – LUKE'S THRILLING GOSPEL

STANDARD PUBLISHING – ...incorporates interesting character sketches, systematic verse studies, and helpful homiletic outlines....organized into sections of expository notes and sections of homilies. The author utilizes a friendly, natural manner of communication which makes this book about the "beloved physician" and his Gospel narrative a complement to anyone's library. DD

THE SWORD OF THE LORD – ...So many outlines on so many topics are presented that it makes the book a treasure chest for preachers. DD

WIERSBE – Don't overlook this fine book. It is filled with treasures of sermon ideas and spiritual truths to help you in your ministry. DD

Thomas, W. H. Griffith – OUTLINE STUDIES IN LUKE

BROOKMAN – Thomas developed these practical sermon outlines from his personal devotional life. It is not a verse-by-verse section outline of Luke's Gospel. G

PACKER – ...a Bible teacher of first rank. His books are pressed down and running over, potent to clear the heads and warm the hearts of those who love the Bible and its Christ. [His books have] classic status...Bible students seeking refreshment and teachers seeking resources will both be delighted.... The author's clear, crisp, straightforward style, joined as it is with wisdom, both theological and devotional, gives his expository works classic status. DD, T

WIERSBE – Griffith Thomas excels in spiritual depth, practicality and a simplicity of expression that make the most profound truths come alive with excitement. DD

JOHN
SEE ALSO "OUR LORD'S PRAYER"

Godet, Frederic L. – COMMENTARY ON JOHN'S GOSPEL
(2 vols. in one)

BARBER – A monumental work by a great theologian and an able defender of the faith. Thorough and exhaustive without being elaborate and verbose.... No preacher should be without it. B, C

BROOKMAN – ...exhaustive.... From a theological and Christological standpoint, Godet has written one of the best works available in print today. G

CUSTER – A very thorough exposition. I

MARTIN – ...has a rich vein of spiritual worth, with practical applications. O

ROSSCUP – A good scholar is at his best here. He is exhaustive and excellent, though this work is old. EE

SMITH – ...from a theological standpoint, and for going to the uttermost depths of the profound teachings recorded in the fourth Gospel, Godet is the supreme work.... Here are some of the finest pages of Christology to be found anywhere; in some paragraphs, truths are so brilliantly set forth that, once read, they will never leave the reader's mind and heart. W

Hengstenberg, E. W. – COMMENTARY ON JOHN   (2 vols.)

BARBER – This study, by the same person who gave us his now famous *Christology of the Old Testament* [see comments, p. 11], is rich in insights, and treats with rare piety the life and labors of Christ. A rewarding work that will handsomely repay the time spent reading it. B, C

BROOKMAN – ...[a] well-balanced, massive commentary on John's Gospel, Hengstenberg develops the life and works of Christ brilliantly from the apostle's writings. This work is a classic.... G

ROSSCUP – This work has much judicious material tying the thought to Old Testament background theology. At times very provocative. EE

SPURGEON – Like others of this author's works: solid, but dry. Y

Powell, Ivor – JOHN'S WONDERFUL GOSPEL

THE BIBLICAL EVANGELIST – Preachers will receive a flood of ideas for sermons from these studies. We do not just refer to the homilies; there are many remarkable outlines and sermon suggestions within the expositions themselves, and Powell inserts excellent word studies within his expository notes, also. DD

NOTHSTINE, S. ELLSWORTH – Dr. Powell, a great Welsh preacher has given us a gold mine on this Gospel!...He possesses a great imagination in his preaching and presents the gospel photographically, which helps the hearers to remember what he has said. DD

PULPIT HELPS – Rarely does one find a commentary on a book of the Bible which has so many helps and insights as this exposition....His exciting use of alliteration provides sermonic seed-thoughts unfolding John's truth with clarity and beauty to stimulate and inspire exposition. DD

WIERSBE – Don't overlook this fine book. It is filled with treasures of sermon ideas and spiritual truths to help you in your ministry. DD

Thomas, David – GOSPEL OF JOHN

MASTERS – Another extremely useful mass of preaching suggestions. P

ACTS

Alexander, Joseph – ACTS OF THE APOSTLES   (2 vols. in one)

BARBER – An exhaustive, thorough exposition that gives valuable help on the meaning of Greek words, defends Stephen's accuracy of chronology in Acts 7, and provides preachers with an abundance of usable material. A warmly devotional treatment. Reformed. B, C

BROOKMAN – [Alexander's] concern...is to promote an exhaustive understanding of the text of Acts and of its message as a whole. G

GRIER – Sound and sober exposition. L

MASTERS – The clear, concentrated note-style of Alexander is perfect for Acts...a most useful and informative commentary. Q

Gloag, Paton J. – CRITICAL AND EXEGETICAL COMMENTARY ON THE ACTS (2 vols.)

BARBER – A thorough exposition based on careful exegesis. Particularly praiseworthy is the writer's handling of critical problems. Warmly recommended. B, C

BROOKMAN – This thorough exposition on the Book of Acts shows a lot of research by an older Scottish Presbyterian minister. The author was not afraid to tackle any problem in the text. G

SPURGEON – Dr. Hackett says of Dr. Gloag's work: "I have examined it with special care. For my purposes I have found it unsurpassed by any similar work in the English language. It shows a thorough mastery of the material: philology, history, and literature pertaining to this range of study, and a skill in the use of this knowledge, which places it in the first class of modern expositions." Y

Laurin, Roy L. – ACTS: Life in Action

BARBER – ...brings out practical applications.... C

BILLY GRAHAM – I have read every book [Dr. Laurin] has ever written. ...many of the thoughts which I use in my preaching have come from [him]. DD

Powell, Ivor – THE AMAZING ACTS

WIERSBE – Don't overlook this fine book. It is filled with treasures of sermon ideas and spiritual truths to help you in your ministry. DD

Stier, Rudolph – THE WORDS OF THE APOSTLES

BARBER – A comprehensive analysis of the speeches and sermons of the Book of Acts. Deserves a place in every expository preacher's library. A must for every student.... B, C

ROSSCUP – ...the work [is] often quite insightful in solid commentary style that delves competently into meaning and implications. EE

SPURGEON – Devout, scholarly, full of thought. To be used discreetly. Y

Walker, Thomas – ACTS OF THE APOSTLES

ROSSCUP – This work...is excellent on problems and detail in general. It is a very helpful commentary. EE

SMITH – ...I consider this the greatest commentary on the Book of Acts written from a missionary standpoint that has been published in our language. The author was a careful student of the Greek text.... Each chapter concludes with a most helpful summary of the teachings of that particular portion of the Word of God. I have never seen this book listed in any bibliography, but it is a treasure house indeed, with much material not to be found in any other commentary on Acts. X

SUGDEN – …a remarkable exposition…has been of tremendous value in my own personal ministry…. I am confident that a great company of those who minister the Word of God will be grateful for the republishing of this refreshing volume…. DD, Z

WIERSBE – …written by a missionary to India, this older work is worth many of the newer books combined. BB

LIVES OF THE APOSTLES, ETC.

Bruce, A. B. – THE TRAINING OF THE TWELVE

BARBER – Unequalled in its field. Shows how Christ disciplined and trained His disciples for the position of apostleship. A most rewarding study. B

BIBLIOTHECA SACRA – Many Christian leaders today still concur with W. H. Griffith Thomas who regarded this volume as "one of the great books of the nineteenth century." It is directed more toward an ongoing life of obedience to Christ than toward the "instant discipleship" that characterizes much of the late twentieth century Christianity. This classic continues to be "must reading" for every Christian. DD

BROOKMAN – …this work…has never been equaled. This classic, learned, practical and inspiring book on the twelve apostles is a must for every minister's library. G

CUSTER – A unique study…not only helps the expositor to instruct his people but also helps him to see his own responsibility before his Lord. I

TED ENGSTROM (as quoted in Jones) – One of the most helpful books on leadership that I've come across…. Without a doubt…one of the finest biblical approaches, and the best teaching known concerning management principles emphasized by the Lord Jesus Christ. M, DD

HOWARD HENDRICKS – A significant book that helped me greatly in the whole area of discipleship. DD

PRARIE OVERCOMER – Bruce's magnificent study…has never been surpassed by any other writer. DD

SMITH – …There is nothing quite as important on the life of our Lord as related to the training of the twelve apostles as this volume. …fresh and inspiring…a classic resource…. It has never been equalled. …it will still be found fresh and inspiring. DD, W

SPURGEON (in *Sword and Trowel*) – A great book, full of suggestions and savour. It should be the companion of every minister. DD

W. H. GRIFFITH THOMAS – One of the great books of the 19th century! DD

WIERSBE – [A] classic that will help you study and preach about the twelve apostles…. This is one book that every pastor ought to take with him on a long holiday and read carefully, not only for insights into the hearts and minds of the apostles, but also for an understanding of the

Master's methods with His men. One of the greatest books on discipleship ever written. cc, dd

Chadwick, W. Edward – THE PASTORAL TEACHING OF PAUL

Barber – ...a rare and valuable volume that every minister should own and refer to repeatedly. c

Wiersbe – I rejoice that this work...is now available to a generation of ministers who read what these chapters present. [Several of these sections] are musts for the pastor who truly wants a spiritual ministry. I know of no volume that treats the "images" of the minister as this one does.... dd

Eadie, John – THE WORDS OF THE APOSTLE PAUL

Barber – Recommended. c

Brookman – ...this study will be valuable to all who seek to understand Paul's discourses and speeches as contained in the Book of Acts. Eadie clearly demonstrates some of the secrets of the early church's dynamic witness. g

Spurgeon – Designed to give ordinary readers a juster and fuller conception of the doctrine and life-work of the apostle. An able work. y

Farrar, Frederic W. – THE LIFE AND WORK OF PAUL (2 vols.)

Barber – ...a priceless asset.... c

Smith – ...brilliantly written.... v

Godet, Frederick L. – STUDIES IN PAUL'S EPISTLES

Brookman – ...still helpful. It is a remarkable treatise on the Epistles of Paul. This work is a classic and contains many excellent discussions. g

Thomas, W. H. Griffith – THE APOSTLE JOHN: His Life and Writings

Barber – A lucid study of the Johannine writings that includes a biographical sketch of the apostle and an extensive analysis of the gospel, epistles, and Revelation. c

Brookman – This outline study is loaded with great teaching and preaching material. g

Arthur L. Farstad – ...a full book, a fine book, and a finely tuned book.... I recommend it heartily to all who wish to learn or teach [this subject]. dd

Packer – The author's clear, crisp, straightforward style, joined as it is with wisdom, both theological and devotional, gives his expository works classic status. dd, t

Wiersbe – Has all the merits for which the author is noted (see comments under Matthew). Griffith Thomas excels in spiritual depth, practicality and a simplicity of expression that make the most profound truths come alive with excitement. CC, DD

Thomas, W. H. Griffith – THE APOSTLE PETER: His Life and Writings

BARBER – Drawing heavily upon Peter's natural characteristics, the writer shows how these were transformed by the Holy Spirit. A timely, devotional study. B

BROOKMAN – ...excellent for devotional study or homiletical use. These outline studies include each event in Peter's life and every verse or chapter in his Epistles. G

PACKER – The author's clear, crisp, straightforward style, joined as it is with wisdom, both theological and devotional, gives his expository works classic status. DD, T

JOHN F. WALVOORD – ...will provide much insight into the noble character of the Apostle Peter...a great work. DD

WIERSBE – ...a good survey of his life that...often [shows] the interesting relationships that exist between Peter in life and his Letters. Griffith Thomas excels in spiritual depth, practicality, and a simplicity of expression that make the most profound truths come alive with excitement. BB, DD

ROMANS

Candlish, Robert S. – STUDIES IN ROMANS 12: The Christian's Sacrifice and Service of Praise

BARBER– There is a treasure trove of riches to be found in this book....Candlish's writing is neither trite nor superficial. Rather, it is an important discussion which skillfully applies sound theology to the interpersonal relationships of every Christian. It is a pleasure to recommend this book to pastors and laypeople alike.... FROM FOREWORD

Haldane, Robert – COMMENTARY ON ROMANS

BARBER – ...has enjoyed a widespread ministry since its first appearance. Brought about a genuine movement of the Spirit.... B

CHALMERS (as quoted by C.H. Spurgeon) – A well-built commentary...solid and congenial food. DD

D. MARTYN LLOYD-JONES – ...I recommend this commentary...for so many reasons. First and foremost is the fact that I have derived such profit and pleasure from it myself....one cannot read it without being conscious of the preacher as well as the expositor. DD

ROSSCUP – ...This is one of the greatest of the older commentaries, almost always offering solid help and much to stimulate the heart. EE

SPURGEON – Dr. Chalmers styled this "a well-built commentary," and strongly recommended it to students of theology. In his "Sabbath Readings" he writes: "I am reading Haldane's *Exposition of the Epistle to the Romans*, and find it solid and congenial food." Y

Laurin, Roy L. – ROMANS: Where Life Begins

BILLY GRAHAM – I have read every book [Dr. Laurin] has ever written.... Many of the thoughts which I use in my preaching have come from [him]. DD

Luther, Martin – COMMENTARY ON ROMANS

BARBER – ...this significant commentary deserves repeated consultation. C

DONALD GREY BARNHOUSE – The fact that Wesley was saved through the instrumentality of Luther's *Romans* gives us sufficient warrant to maintain this old work in modern form. Beyond question, Luther's *Romans* is one of the great books of Christian history and well deserves the devotional reading by believers. DD

CHILDS – ...Luther's robust and profound commentaries offer an inexhaustible resource for the proclamation of the gospel. H

MASTERS – A great classic. Perhaps every preacher should have at least this commentary by Luther. He loved this epistle, and his unique and distinctive style is most effective here. P

DUKE MCCALL – ...obviously a "must" for every preacher's library. DD

J. THEODORE MUELLER – Luther's *Romans* deserves general study, not only because of its vast devotional material, but also because of its clear and sharp emphasis on salvation by grace through faith in Christ. Fraught with profound thoughts, it witnesses everywhere to the sincere piety of the great Reformer. DD

JOHN WESLEY – In the evening I went very unwillingly to a society in Aldersgate Street, where one was reading Luther's Preface to the *Epistle to the Romans*. About a quarter before nine, while he was describing the change which God works in the heart through faith in Christ, I felt my heart strangely warmed. I felt I did trust Christ, Christ alone, for my salvation; and an assurance was given me that He had taken my sins away, even mine, and saved me from the law of sin and death. DD

Olshausen, Hermann – STUDIES IN ROMANS

BARBER – ...may still be read with profit. C

Pridham, Arthur – NOTES ON ROMANS

SPURGEON – Sound and gracious, but somewhat dull. Y

Robinson, Thomas – STUDIES IN ROMANS

SPURGEON – A good book in a good style. Worth any amount to preachers. Y

MASTERS – ...a word-by-word commentary which concentrates into terse notes the views of all leading commentators and supplements them with numerous applications, ideas and "leads" to stir the thinking of preachers.... The sheer quantity of information, doctrinal observation and spiritual suggestion against individual words would fill five or six volumes if written up in a more formal style. I have frequently used and proved this...volume over twenty years and warmly recommend it as a

great aid to preachers. A wonderful commentary, highly recommended.
DD, P, O

Scroggie, W. Graham – SALVATION AND BEHAVIOR: Romans 1—8; 12—15

BARBER – Brief devotional studies. Recommended. C

WIERSBE – Valuable.... How that man could preach and teach the Word of God! DD

FIRST AND SECOND CORINTHIANS

Candlish, Robert S. – STUDIES IN FIRST CORINTHIANS 15: Life in a Risen Savior

BARBER – ...noteworthy for its clarity, careful exposition of the text, and balanced application of biblical truth to the life of the believer. C

BROOKMAN – Candlish knew how to...apply truth to everyday living. G

Edwards, Thomas C. – FIRST CORINTHIANS

BARBER – One of the truly great commentaries on the Greek text. Of inestimable value. Remains one of the best discussions extant. This work is truly meritorious and deserves a place...in the library of every pastor's library. B, C

BROOKMAN – ...a rich, verse-by-verse, conservative exposition. G

Godet, Frederic L. – COMMENTARY ON FIRST CORINTHIANS

ALLISON – ...restores a treasure to the hands of modern Bible students. ...he offers some of the best background information on the cultural and moral climate of Corinth. A

BARBER – Scholarly, exegetical comments on the text and theme of the epistle make this work one of the outstanding treatments of all time. B

BROOKMAN – Godet's commentary on First Corinthians is one of the best in print today. A careful reading of this exegetical work will pay rich dividends. G

MASTERS – ...Godet was best known for his works on Luke and this epistle.... Full of exegetical help, very technical, yet endowed with practical comment. P

ROSSCUP – ...one of the finer works among the older commentaries, well-worth consulting... EE

Laurin, Roy L. – FIRST CORINTHIANS: Where Life Matures

BILLY GRAHAM – I have read every book [Dr. Laurin] has ever written.... Many of the thoughts which I use in my preaching have come from [him]. DD

Laurin, Roy L. – SECOND CORINTHIANS: Where Life Endures

BARBER – With genuine devotional warmth, Laurin explains how life endures and matures in accordance with the plans and purposes of God. C

BILLY GRAHAM – I have read every book [Dr. Laurin] has ever written.... Many of the thoughts which I use in my preaching have come from [him]. DD

Olshaussen, Hermann – FIRST AND SECOND CORINTHIANS

BARBER – Said W. Lindsay Alexander, "Highly esteemed for his happy combinations of grammatico-historical exegesis, with spiritual insight into the meaning of the sacred writings." B

PHILIP SCHAFF (as quoted by Barber) – Pays careful attention to the theological exposition.... C

Scroggie, W. Graham – THE LOVE LIFE: A Study of 1 Corinthians 13

BARBER – A valuable, devotional work. B

WIERSBE – Valuable. How that man could preach and teach the Word of God! DD

GALATIANS

Luther, Martin – COMMENTARY ON GALATIANS

(Translated by Erasmus Middleton, ed. by John P. Fallowes)

ALLISON – ...this commentary gives us an intimate view of the Bible study that shaped Luther's life-work. A

JOHN BUNYAN – I do prefer this book...excepting the whole Bible, before all books I have ever seen. DD

CHILDS – ...Luther's robust and profound commentaries offer an inexhaustible resource for the proclamation of the gospel. H

MASTERS – A fine reprint of this classic. P

ROSSCUP – ....Much of the heart-pulse of Luther's stand for justification by faith appears here. EE

SPURGEON – This is a great historic work, and is beyond criticism, on account of its great usefulness. As a commentary, its accuracy might be questioned; but for emphatic utterances and clear statements of the great doctrine of the epistle it remains altogether by itself, and must be judged per se. Y

EPHESIANS

Moule, H. C. G. – STUDIES IN EPHESIANS

ALLISON – Here is a good devotional commentary. A

BARBER – A devotional masterpiece full of comfort and exhortation. B

BROOKMAN – ...valuable for Bible students today. G

CUSTER – A warmly devotional exposition. I

MASTER – A much more devotional work...a useful companion.... P

SUGDEN – ...anything [Moule] writes will bless you. Z

TENNEY (as quoted by Merchant) – [A] profound commentary. R, AA

WIERSBE – ...a standard commentary [on this book]. ...helpful in the Greek, very devotional and very practical. BB, DD

Powell, Ivor – THE EXCITING EPISTLE TO THE EPHESIANS

BIBLICAL EVANGELIST – This is an excellent volume, well worth your investment. DD

MESSENGER MAGAZINE – ...Here is alliterative outlining carried to perfection. His insight into Scripture is amazing, but so practical. You will not want to preach or teach Ephesians without having this work at your side. DD

WIERSBE – Don't overlook [this] fine book. It is filled with treasures of sermon ideas and spiritual truths to help you in your ministry. DD

Westcott, Brooke Foss – EPISTLE TO THE EPHESIANS

BARBER – A widely acclaimed work. Deserving of the same attention given his other works. B, C

BROOKMAN – For those who want to do some serious exegetical study on Ephesians, Westcott's commentary is a must. G

CUSTER – A...very valuable study. I

PHILIPPIANS

Hutchinson, John – AN EXPOSITION OF PHILIPPIANS

BARBER – ...traces with care the unfolding of Paul's thought and applies the principles that are laid bare to the needs of believers. This is an excellent volume, perspicuous and practical. C

Laurin, Roy L. – PHILIPPIANS: Where Life Advances

BILLY GRAHAM – I have read every book [Dr. Laurin] has ever written.... Many of the thoughts which I use in my preaching have come from [him]. DD

Meyer, F. B. – DEVOTIONAL COMMENTARY ON PHILIPPIANS

BARBER – Textual messages, devotional and edifying. B

BROOKMAN – This verse-by-verse devotional commentary is inspirational and challenging. It is a series of textual sermons that exhibit a combination of thorough scholarship and practical application. G

MASTERS – Full of application.... P

ROSSCUP – ....Lay persons as well as pastors and Bible teachers looking for a work that speaks to the heart and offers many insights into a deeper maturity in commitments of faith will find this a fresh breath. EE

WIERSBE – ...a helpful study. BB

Moule, H. C. G. – STUDIES IN PHILIPPIANS

BARBER – A beautifully written, deeply devotional treatment expounding the affectionate character of this epistle and relating its message to the lives of believers. B

SUGDEN – ...anything [Moule] writes will bless you. Z

TENNEY (as quoted by Merchant) – Precipitates the beauty and light of the Scriptures. R, AA

WIERSBE – ...a helpful study. ...very devotional and very practical. BB, DD

Vaughan, Charles John – EPISTLE TO THE PHILIPPIANS

BROOKMAN – Vaughn's expository messages on this epistle are considered classic. Ministers will welcome this valuable reprint for help in preparing a series of sermons on the Book of Philippians. G

SPURGEON – Deservedly esteemed. Dr. Vaughan gives a literal translation of his text from the original Greek, and then expounds it, believing it, as he says, "to be the duty of every Christian teacher to assist his congregation in drinking, not of the stream only, but at the spring of revealed truth." Y

COLOSSIANS AND PHILEMON

Eadie, John – COLOSSIANS

BARBER – First published over a century ago, this rich and inspiring exposition is one that preachers who have a knowledge of Greek will appreciate for its insights and detailed explanations. B

BROOKMAN – This work is valuable for its exposition and its study of the original text. A helpful, classic reprint. G

CUSTER – A very thorough expositon of the Greek text. I

WIERSBE – ...a standard commentary. BB

Laurin, Roy L. – COLOSSIANS: Where Life Is Established

BILLY GRAHAM – I have read every book [Dr. Laurin] has ever written.... Many of the thoughts which I use in my preaching have come from [him]. DD

Moule, H. C. G. – STUDIES IN COLOSSIANS AND PHILEMON

ALLISON – Evangelical readers will prefer this volume. A

BARBER – Moule was known for his saintliness and evangelical fervor. These studies bear testimony to his ability as an expositor. They deal adequately with the text and deftly apply the message of these epistles. One of the most reverent and delightful of expositions extant. By all means buy it. **B, C**

BROOKMAN – Moule's commentary on the English text. ...a valuable, practical exposition. **G**

CUSTER – Warmly devotional exposition. **I**

MASTERS – A very useful "second commentary" with devotional application. **P**

SUGDEN – ...anything [Moule] writes will bless you. **Z**

TENNEY (as quoted by Merchant) – [A] rewarding and glowing commentary. **R, AA**

WIERSBE – ...a deeply devotional commentary based on a profound knowledge of the Greek text. **BB, DD**

Nicholson, William – COLOSSIANS: Oneness With Christ

BARBER – ...combines outstanding scholarship with deeply devotional spirit. **G**

BROOKMAN – Here are some valuable expository lectures. ...a combination of outstanding scholarship and an excellent devotional tone. Highly regarded by Dr. Wilbur M. Smith. **G**

CUSTER – Rich devotional expositions...combine[s] real scholarship with devotional warmth. **I**

JAMES M. GRAY – The feast of my own soul in the perusal of [this book] I am impatient to share with as large a constituency of my fellow-brethren as I can possibly reach, for such teaching, as to its deep insight into spiritual things, its rigor of appeal, its heavenly unction, its grace of manner and beauty of diction, is not commonly met with in this day or any other day. **DD**

SMITH – ...in no other book in our language are there such wonderful expositions on certain passages in this Epistle. ...these lectures came from the heart and mind of an intellectual and spiritual giant; they will communicate power and inspiration to every one who carefully, expectantly reads them. **W**

Scroggie, W. Graham – STUDIES IN PHILEMON

BARBER – A rewarding and in-depth study. One of the best ever produced on this epistle...remains one of the best ever written on...Philemon. **B, C**

BROOKMAN – A worthy devotional and expositional study on Philemon by a gifted writer. This is a rewarding in-depth study of a very neglected book of the Bible. Conservative. **G**

WIERSBE – Valuable...How that man could preach and teach the Word of God! **DD**

Thomas, W. H. Griffith – STUDIES IN COLOSSIANS AND PHILEMON

CUSTER – Devotional expositions. **I**

PACKER – The author's clear, crisp, straightforward style, joined as it is with wisdom, both theological and devotional, gives his expository works classic status. **DD, T**

WIERSBE – [From] one of the spiritual giants of his day [comes] one of the best expositions available, not only for the advanced student, but also for the average believer who wants to gain a working knowledge of [these] important epistles.... Deeply spiritual and very practical. Griffith Thomas excels in spiritual depth, practicality and a simplicity of expression that make the most profound truths come alive with excitement. **BB, DD**

THESSALONIAN EPISTLES

Marsh, F. E. – PRACTICAL TRUTHS FROM FIRST THESSALONIANS

SUGDEN – ...a wealth of enrichment for our spiritual lives. I am personally grateful that this volume...has been made available.... **DD, Z**

Milligan, George – PAUL'S EPISTLES TO THE THESSALONIANS

BARBER – A brilliantly written, critical study that must of necessity take second place to more recent works. However, it is worth consulting. Amillennial. **B, C**

BROOKMAN – ...an outstanding New Testament writer. This exegetical work includes a good summary on the person of the Antichrist. **G**

CUSTER – The best commentary on the Greek text. **I**

THE PASTORAL EPISTLES

Liddon, H. P. – THE FIRST EPISTLE TO TIMOTHY

BARBER – A competent treatment based upon a grammatical analysis of the Greek text. Excellent. Serves as a model of good expository preparation. **B**

BROOKMAN – Even though it is based on the Greek text, a minister without a knowledge of the original language can still profit from this book. **G**

Moule, H. C. G. – STUDIES IN SECOND TIMOTHY

BARBER – A delightful devotional commentary. **C**

BROOKMAN – ...a devotional classic worth consulting. **G**

WIERSBE – A fine [commentary]...helpful in the Greek, very devotional and very practical. **DD**

SUGDEN – ...anything [Moule] writes will bless you. **Z**

Rowland, Alfred – STUDIES IN FIRST TIMOTHY

THE ENGLISH CHURCHMAN (as quoted by Barber) – We may say it is a work of no ordinary value, and Christians will find it a rich foast. It is needless, of course, to say that [this study] is a work of a scholar; it is also the work of a whole-hearted believer and its design was intended for the use of all who love the Lord in simplicity and truth. C

Stock, Eugene – PRACTICAL TRUTHS FROM THE PASTORAL EPISTLES

SMITH – ...every pastor ought to study these fifty chapters carefully. W

WIERSBE – No book on pastoral theology, based on the Pastoral Epistles, contains more practical application, and is more of a delight to read. DD

Taylor, Thomas – AN EXPOSITION OF TITUS

BARBER – A Puritan commentary that readily explores the inner reality of Paul's letter to his youthful associate. C

BROOKMAN – ...extensive...it will still be helpful to the Bible student and minister. G

SPURGEON – The title page calls Thomas Taylor "a famous and most elaborate divine." He was a preacher at Paul's Cross during the reigns of Elizabeth and James I and a voluminous writer. This commentary will well repay the reader. Y

HEBREWS

Anderson, Sir Robert – TYPES IN HEBREWS

BARBER – A rewarding study that evangelical Christians can ill afford to neglect. C

Bruce, A. B. – THE EPISTLE TO THE HEBREWS

BARBER – An exhaustive interpretation of the epistle based on the premise that it is a formal defense of the Christian faith. Preachers will find this a most helpful exposition. B, C

Bullinger, E. W. – GREAT CLOUD OF WITNESSES IN HEBREWS 11

BARBER – An extensive expository treatment frequently provides discerning explanations of Greek words and their origin. Preachers will find these studies helpful. B

BROOKMAN – A complete exposition of Hebrews chapter 11 dealing with the heroes of the faith. ...is still very helpful. G

WIERSBE – Bullinger was a great student of the Word of God...a must for your library. I know of no other book on Hebrews 11 in the English language that contains more solid spiritual teaching and practical truth. DD

Edwards, Thomas C. – THE EPISTLE TO THE HEBREWS

BARBER – An excellent, easy-to-follow discussion of the purpose of the epistle. Serves to give laypeople as well as those looking for a theological development of a central theme exactly what they need. **B, C**

BROOKMAN – [Edwards] blends careful exposition and application. **G**

Moule, H. C. G. – STUDIES IN HEBREWS

WIERSBE – A fine [commentary]...helpful in the Greek, very devotional and very practical. **DD**

SUGDEN – ...anything [Moule] writes will bless you. **Z**

Owen, John – HEBREWS (7 vols. condensed into one)

ALLISON – Thomas Chalmers called this commentary "a work of gigantic strength as well as gigantic size." **A**

LOCKYER – ...a mine of truth. The most outstanding of Owen's works. **DD, N**

MASTERS – The major contribution on Hebrews.... Though hard to believe, the greatly shortened version retains all the rich argument and sense of the expository parts of the 7-volume original work. With such a paperback available, it simply makes no sense for preachers NOT to have Owen on Hebrews. **P**

SMITH – The most exhaustive work ever written on Hebrews is *The Exposition of the Epistle to the Hebrews*, by that great Puritan divine, John Owen.... **DD**

Saphir, Adolph – EPISTLE TO THE HEBREWS

BARBER – Expository studies by a converted Jew. **C**

CUSTER – Fervent, warmhearted messages on Hebrews by a converted Jew. **I**

LOCKYER – Without doubt, Saphir's most satisfying *Epistle to the Hebrews* is a masterpiece.... We most heartily commend this...to all Bible lovers. **DD, N**

ROSSCUP – Careful insight into the text and fine articulation for the meaning by a Hebrew Christian. **EE**

SMITH – ...one of the finest expository works in our language, exceptionally rich from a devotional standpoint, and should stand on the shelves of every Bible student's library. **W**

SPURGEON – Mr. Saphir has always something to say worthy of the attention of spiritual minds. His mind finds a track of its own, but he is never speculative. We always enjoy his remarks, though he is not specially terse or brilliant. **Y**

WIERSBE – ...excellent. **DD**

JAMES

Johnstone, Robert – LECTURES ON JAMES

ALLISON – It is a good introduction to James for a beginning Bible student. **A**

BARBER – One of the few works of its kind. Makes rich, rewarding reading. Suitable for both pastor and informed layperson. A must for the expository preacher. B, C

BROOKMAN – Johnstone brings together a balanced exposition, both practical and exegetical, on this important epistle. Very helpful.... G

CUSTER – A strong exposition. I

MASTERS – ...derived from sermons and is very readable and strongly applied.... A most valuable commentary. Q

ROSSCUP – ...Johnstone has produced a very helpful work for the English reader which is based to a large extent upon a sound knowledge of the Greek text. EE

SPURGEON – A very useful, scholarly, and readable book. Y

WIERSBE – I have enjoyed using [this] work. BB

Mayor, Joseph – THE EPISTLE OF ST. JAMES

ALLISON – ...an in-depth study of James, complete with the Greek text and a full array of textual notes....This commentary is best for the advanced student who would like to peruse the Greek, phrase by phrase. A

BARBER – A work of massive scholarship that ranks among the most important exegetical works ever produced on this Epistle. C

ROSSCUP – ...this commentary of more than 600 pages gives the reader almost 300 pages in introductory explorations about the identity of the writer James...the relations to other New Testament books, grammar and style, etc. It is a work of towering scholarship and exhaustive detail. From the standpoint of the Greek text it is one of the best on James. EE

Smith – Without any question at all, the most important commentary on this difficult portion of the New Testament ever to be issued is this volume. When the minister comes to the time when he desires to expound this Epistle, he will find Mayor indispensable. W

A. F. WALLS (GUIDE TO CHRISTIAN READING, IVP) – ...a very thorough commentary on the Greek text. DD

Stier, Rudolf E. – COMMENTARY ON JAMES

BARBER – ...of value to preachers as well as laypeople. C

BROOKMAN – ...helpful. ...a series of expository messages on the Epistle of James. G

SPURGEON – No one can be expected to receive all that Stier has to say, but he must be dull indeed who can not learn much from him. Read with care; he is a great instructor. Y

FIRST AND SECOND PETER

Luther, Martin – COMMENTARY ON PETER AND JUDE

BARBER – These studies challenge the spiritual laxity of our times and call us back to the principles that led to the Reformation. C

CHILDS – ...Luther's robust and profound commentaries offer an inexhaustible resource for the proclamation of the gospel. H

MASTERS – Simple exposition, very practical; a pastor's heart evident in meaningful communication with his people. Q

SPURGEON – In Luther's racy style. One of his best productions. Copies are scarce as white elephants... Y

EPISTLES OF JOHN

Candlish, Robert – FIRST EPISTLE OF JOHN

BARBER – Expository messages presenting a moving portrait of Christ and the believer's relationship to Him. A true classic. B, C

BROOKMAN – ...the classic work on the First Epistle of John. It is clear, concise and practical. G

CUSTER – An exhaustive exposition of surprising fervency. ...combine[s] real scholarship with devotional warmth. I

MASTERS – Without a doubt the best available work on First John. This volume towers above the others.... This "commentary" is actually a series of 46 brilliant lectures. They are highly readable and literally full of experimental material. This is an essential commentary for preachers and teachers. Q

ROSSCUP – ....one of the better older commentaries on 1 John...It is penetrating in its devotional depths which search the reader's heart... EE

SMITH – ...I have been frequently amazed to find how few ministers, even those who have been preaching for some years, have ever heard of this work.... These lectures go to the very depths of the truths set forth in this precious, inexhaustible, and not always easily understoood Epistle of the Beloved Apostle. Some pages here seem to be almost perfect. The book will search one's heart, it will lift him up into new heights, where he will see with greater clearness than ever before some of the precious privileges and obligations of the child of God. It is a work to turn to frequently for inspiration and strength.... My own opinion is that the richest exposition of the First Epistle of John is still that series of lectures [of] the *First Epistle of John*. ...this volume became very scarce in the early part of our century, but fortunately it has since then been reprinted. W, X

SPURGEON – We set great store by these lectures. A man hardly needs anything beyond Candlish. He is devout, candid, prudent, and forcible. Y

WIERSBE – If you have not read Candlish's remarkable exposition on 1 John, by all means do—prayerfully. CC

Findlay, George G. - STUDIES IN JOHN'S EPISTLES

BARBER – An outstanding exposition....Dedicated scholarship is combined with rare spiritual insight, making this a first-rate work. B

MARTIN – Unreservedly commended.... o

MASTERS – ...an important work with a careful kind of style. P

ROSSCUP – Based on the Greek text, his work is one of the great commentaries on the three Epistles... EE

TENNEY – A rich exposition of the three Epistles. R

Laurin, Roy L. – FIRST JOHN: Life at Its Best

BILLY GRAHAM – I have read every book [Dr. Laurin] has ever written.... Many of the thoughts which I use in my preaching have come from [him]. DD

Lias, John J. – THE FIRST EPISTLE OF JOHN

BARBER – A conservative and scholarly exposition defending the genuineness of the epistle and containing some valuable exegetical insights. One of the finest exegetical and expository works for preachers. B, C

JUDE

Manton, Thomas – COMMENTARY ON JUDE

BARBER – ...very extensive, as can be seen from the fact that this exposition covers 375 pages. B

BROOKMAN – Manton's work on Jude is a classic. G

CUSTER – An exhaustive...exposition. I

MASTERS – ...[a] full and rewarding Puritan commentary.... P

SPURGEON – Manton's work is most commendable. Y

REVELATION

Bullinger, E. W. – COMMENTARY ON REVELATION

BARBER – ...offers a uniquely different interpretation of the Apocalypse. C

ROSSCUP – The Greek student will find this a very good commentary generally... EE

Scott, Walter – EXPOSITION OF THE REVELATION OF JESUS CHRIST

BARBER – ...gives evidence of intensive research, careful exposition, and an awareness of God's plan for the future. Strongly typological. B

ROSSCUP – A helpful premillennial work that is lucid in expounding the meaning. EE

SMITH – If I were asked what one volume I would suggest for the layreader for an understanding of the Book of Revelation, I would recommend the work by Walter Scott.... DD

WIERSBE – ...among the commentaries I keep nearby.... A classic treatment of the English text. BB, DD

Seiss, Joseph A. – THE APOCALYPSE: Exposition of the Book of the Revelation

BARBER – An exhaustive, premillennial exposition by a well-known Lutheran writer of the past century. **B**

CUSTER – Powerful messages.... **I**

SMITH – ...the most famous expository work on Revelation in our language, and no minister intending to preach an extended series of sermons from the Book of Revelation can afford to be without it. ...sane, suggestive, reverent, and, on the whole, dependable. There is no man in the English world today, as far as we know,...who is equipped both with a knowledge of the Word and a gift of oratory, to deliver such a series of lectures as these which are found in these some five hundred pages. **U**

WIERSBE – ...a helpful commentary. **BB**

Tucker, W. Leon – STUDIES IN REVELATION

FAIR – ...one of the most well-structured commentaries...on Revelation that has ever been published.... Prayerfully and carefully written...contains a goldmine of handy and rare information.... **DD, K**

SECTION IV
OTHER SUBJECTS

APOLOGETICS

Orr, James – THE CHRISTIAN VIEW OF GOD AND THE WORLD

BAPTIST EXAMINER – ...has long been a classic in the area of apologetics. It may well be the best single volume on this subject. DD

BARBER – ...relevant and useful. Should be purchased. B

BEREA BAPTIST BANNER – An extensive description and defense of the Theistic world view centering in the incarnation of Jesus Christ. A classic Christocentric interpretation of existence and reality. DD

GROUNDS (Eternity Magazine) – ...exhilarated my spirit as it stretched my mind. [Orr] freed me from the haunting suspicion that belief in the gospel must be maintained by faith alone in defiance of learning and logic. DD

ROBERT FLINT, quoted by Wilbur M. Smith, (*His* Magazine) – It is admirable in conception, plan, spirit, and exhortation; and a truly noble and most valuable contribution to theological literature. DD

Smith, Wilbur M. – THEREFORE STAND

BARBER – An apologetic for biblical Christianity that was one of the best works available when it first appeared. B

BROOKMAN – This work has never been superseded. It stands among the best in the field of apologetics. Evangelical. G

HAROLD J. OCKENGA – The influence of Dr. Smith's...writings...will go on to benefit young women and men, who wish to proclaim the Lord. Many are the testimonies of those who have been established through his positive teaching. DD

Torrey, R.A. (ed.) – THE FUNDAMENTALS

THE BANNER – ...can be unreservedly recommended. DD

BAPTIST SUNDAY SCHOOL BOARD – ...for certain, [it] belongs in the library of every thoughtful Bible student. DD

BARBER – The famous *Fundamentals* that first appeared in 1909 are here revised and edited for republication. B

HENRY, CARL F.H. (*Christianity Today*) – ...discloses many evidences of evangelical strengths. Here one finds polemic without bitterness, and a concentration upon great issues.... DD

NIX (*The Fundamentalist Journal*) – The Fundamentals are as relevant as ever. They provide a model of work and witness of lasting value. DD

PACKER – ...expound[s] and defend[s] the evangelical faith. T

SOUTHERN PRESBYTERIAN JOURNAL – ...there is an immense wealth of Christian truth presented here in a convincing manner. DD

SUNDAY SCHOOL TIMES – ...a veritable library of precious truth. DD

BAPTISM

Carson, Alexander – BAPTISM

BARBER – A full discussion on the proper subjects of baptism, as well as a vigorous plea for the immersion of believers...a welcome and important contribution.... B, C

GRIER – ...remains one of the strongest and ablest statements.... L

BIBLE CHARACTERS

Edersheim, Alfred – PRACTICAL TRUTHS FROM ELISHA

BARBER – ...this book is worthy of diligent reading. C

BROOKMAN – A classic...giving a complete scriptural account of the life and work of the prophet Elisha, featuring thorough research, solid exposition and spiritual application. G

SPURGEON – This author is always interesting, showing close acquaintance with Jewish customs, and knowing how to utilize his information. Y

WIERSBE – [Contains] rich veins of gold that others have ignored or neglected. I rejoice that [this] classic is available again for people who are serious about Bible study. ...you [will] find insights from the Scriptures that can enrich your life and ministry.... DD

Kirk, Thomas – THE LIFE OF JOSEPH

BARBER – Of utmost value for the pastor who preaches on Bible characters...a work that preachers will want to refer to again and again. B, C

BROOKMAN – This is an excellent treatment of the great life of Joseph. Kirk shows diligent research, painstaking detail and considerable insight in these studies. The homiletical helps are abundant in this volume. G

Matheson, George – Bible Portraits Series
PORTRAITS OF BIBLE WOMEN
PORTRAITS OF BIBLE MEN (1st series)
PORTRAITS OF BIBLE MEN (2nd series)
PORTRAITS OF BIBLE MEN (3rd series)

THE BANNER – ...If you want to understand better God's dealings with his people, Matheson will guide you. DD

BAPTIST EXAMINER – ...a very spiritual writer. He sees beneath the surface into the deep spiritual values of the lives of Bible Characters....But more than this, he applies the spiritual lessons learned there from, to the lives of the reader. DD

BAPTIST STANDARD – This is, indeed, a masterful publication that warrants your utmost attention in living the Christian life. DD

CHRISTIAN OBSERVER – ...You will find in this volume a wealth of devotional enrichment. The prayers in themselves are worth the price of the book, but each prayer finds its roots in the characterization of a transformed sinner. DD

WIERSBE – In this series...this...blind scholar-preacher saw more than most of us who see! No evangelical writer, including the great Alexander Whyte, surpasses Matheson in...Bible biography. BB, DD

Vander Velde, Frances – WOMEN OF THE BIBLE

BARBER – ...this volume has stood the test of time. Thirty-one stimulating, imaginative, and devotional studies of women of the Old and New Testaments. Ideal material for discussion groups. Should be consulted when teaching or preaching on the women of the Bible. B, C

Whyte, Alexander – BIBLE CHARACTERS FROM THE OLD AND NEW TESTAMENT (complete in one volume)

ALLISON – Whyte has a colorful way of recreating Bible characters. Though he did not have access to the discoveries of archaeologist in this century, Whyte did have a brilliant imagination and a marvelous gift for narrative writing. This book is a joy to read. A

BARBER – An epochal work that increases in value the more it is used. B

BROOKMAN – This is one of the best books on Bible characters to be found anywhere. G

GRIER – Whyte has much that is striking and illuminating.... . L

BEN HADEN – Through the Scriptures I first met the characters of the Bible. But only through Alexander Whyte have I come to know them. Next to the Bible I find *Bible Characters* by Alexander Whyte the greatest help in understanding the men and women in God's Word. ...My life is richer for reading this man. *Bible Characters* is biography at its best. DD

DAVID R. MAINS – In his *Bible Characters*, Whyte's imaginative skills amaze and delight. Time and again, you are convinced he must have known these people personally, and if not these specific men and women, then certainly he understood human nature intimately well. DD

SMITH – For the study of Bible biographies, you should secure…a marvelous series by Alexander Whyte, one of the great preachers in the world of a generation ago… . No one has analyzed these characters so vividly and penetrating as Whyte. Every page is edifying and suggestive. …if I can stir up a few of my younger friends…to gather to themselves everything that Whyte has ever written which they can secure…and I know that they in turn were being daily refreshed. …there is nothing to compare with it in the English language, and I doubt if there is in any language. Some of these chapters will send one weeping to one's knees; others will make one shudder; others will drive one into the pulpit to preach with new power, new conviction, and new fervor. … By all means lay hold of this set, and do not let it collect dust, but read the pages, and let them mold, and master and mature you. Oh, for more men like Whyte today! U, V, W

WIERSBE – *Bible Characters* is a collection of the great preacher's messages which focus on one key aspect of the subject's personality and uses that to illumine his life. BB

BIBLE STUDY

Bullinger, E. W. – NUMBER IN SCRIPTURE

WIERSBE – I find myself referring to this work. One need not agree with all of Bullinger's views to benefit from his work. DD

SUGDEN – …a great book. Z

Burton, Ernest DeWitt – SYNTAX OF THE MOODS AND TENSES IN NEW TESTAMENT GREEK

BARBER – …is still of inestimable value to students of Greek and contains one of the best treatments on the translation of direct and indirect discourse available. B, C

DANKER – …clamors for attention. …still holds the field as a lucid presentation of an often elusive subject. J

Fausset, Andrew R. – HOME BIBLE STUDY DICTIONARY

APPELMAN, HYMAN J. – …not only an encyclopedia and dictionary, but really it is a compendium of sermonic material. DD

MOODY MONTHLY – …probably the best one-volume Bible encyclopedia ever prepared…contains around a million words. DD

THE WORLD OF BOOKS – …Dr. Fausset was a diligent and thorough scholar, richly endowed in mind and spirit. This volume is the harvest of his painstaking toils. DD

NAZARENE MINISTER'S BOOK CLUB – A comprehensive Bible dictionary by a co-author of the Jamieson, Fausset and Brown Bible Commentary....It could be enthusiastically recommended to Bible students and Sunday School teachers. **DD**

CHRISTIAN HOME AND SCHOOL MAGAZINE – ...a very handy book of reference....is a time saver, for it has information on all Biblical subjects arranged in alphabetical order. **DD**

Spurgeon, Charles Haddon – COMMENTING AND COMMENTARIES: A Reference Guide to Book Buying
(Newly Updated Edition)

BARBER – ...An extensive catalog of Bible commentaries and other expository works. Of particular value for its listing of works from the time of the Reformation to the middle of the nineteenth century. Emphasis is placed on those works making relevant application of truth to life. **B, C**

CHILDS – ...I consider Charles H. Spurgeon's *Commenting and Commentaries* a real classic...he...had much skill and common sense in discerning the enduring qualities of excellence. **H**

SMITH – Every minister ought to have in his library Charles H. Spurgeon's famous, helpful and fascinating work, *Commenting and Commentaries.* ...a remarkable piece of work for anyone preaching to such great audiences as Spurgeon, whose sermons were published every week, and who continued for years to edit the *Sword and Trowel.* ...the most widely used bibliography of commentaries on the Scriptures.... There are over [1,400] volumes listed in this unique annotated bibliography. **U, W**

Wilson, William – NEW WILSON'S OLD TESTAMENT WORD STUDIES (New edition keyed to *Strong's Concordance* and *The Theological Wordbook of the Old Testament*)

BROOKMAN – ...a valuable tool for both the Hebrew student and those who do not have a working knowledge of the language, offering an aid for the understanding of word meanings and help in understanding difficult passages. It is both an exhaustive dictionary and a concordance in that significant English words are translated from more than one original Hebrew word have a listing of major Scripture references coded to each original Hebrew word used. The book is arranged in English alphabetical order, giving every Hebrew word its literal English meaning. **G**

WIERSBE – One of the most helpful Hebrew concordances that I have. It's a wonderful shortcut to help me in getting to those Hebrew words. This new edition is one hundred times more useful than it was before. **DD**

SUGDEN – ...the greatest book that has been published recently.... **Z**

BIBLIOLOGY

Saphir, Adolph – DIVINE UNITY OF SCRIPTURE
BARBER – ...readers of Scripture will benefit greatly... c
SMITH – ...a classic work. v

BIOGRAPHY

Wesley, John – THE HEART OF WESLEY'S JOURNAL
ROBERT E. COLEMAN – As a self-portrait of Wesley, this remarkable composition shows better than anything else the manner of man he was, and the temper of the times in which he lived. DD
KAUFFMAN – ...highlights the labors of the founder of Methodism...provides interesting data on the culture and customs of the times. DD
MALEFYT – ...provides insight into a towering leader who changed a nation's social patterns and affected its history in a crisis period of history not unlike our own. R
MASTERS – ...informative and challenging. DD

CHRISTOLOGY
SEE ALSO "LIFE OF JESUS CHRIST"

Anderson, Sir Robert – THE LORD FROM HEAVEN
BARBER – A study of the deity of Christ, with particular emphasis on His messiahship and His role as "King of kings and Lord of lords".... A refreshing study of Christ's deity.... B, C

Andrews, Samuel J. & Gifford, Edwin Hamilton – THE INCARNATION OF CHRIST (*Man and the Incarnation* and *The Incarnation: Phil. 2:5-11 & Psalm 110*, 2 vols. in one)
BARBER – Indispensable to a minister's library. c
BROOKMAN – An excellent combination of two classic works on the incarnation. This book shows that Jesus Christ is the incarnate Son of God—very God and very man. G

Dalman, Gustaf H. – THE WORDS OF CHRIST
BARBER – A series of studies on a wide variety of themes ranging from a consideration of God's theocracy to the evasive modes post-exilic Jews used in referring to God. Includes Jewish eschatological belief and essays dealing with "Son of Man," "Son of God," "Christ," and the Semitic idea of kingship inherent in the "Son of David." B, C
BROOKMAN – An excellent volume.... G

Horne, Herman Harrell – TEACHING TECHNIQUES OF JESUS: How Jesus Taught

BARBER – Pastors today need to learn from the teaching techniques of Jesus Christ. This book is designed to stimulate such a study and deserves a place on every pastor's desk. B

THE PRARIE OVERCOMER – It's a classic. For Christian leaders it is "must" reading, because it deals with the whole process of how Jesus trained His disciples. DD

Ramsay, William H. – THE EDUCATION OF CHRIST

BARBER – An informative, historical study that makes a unique contribution to our knowledge of the time. B

EDWARD M. BLAIKLOCK – Its pages will serve as an introduction to the man, and his insight into that strong interweaving of place and time, of stage and circumstance, which were part of his [Ramsay's] contribution to ancient studies. They may never be separated again. DD

Thomas, W. H. Griffith – CHRISTIANITY IS CHRIST

BARBER – Centers on the person and work of Christ, vindicates the uniqueness of His character and mission, establishes the credibility of the gospel records, and deals convincingly with the meaning of and need for His bodily resurrection. A most important volume. B

BROOKMAN – ...[a] good older work. G

CHURCH MINISTRIES

Brooks, Phillips – THE JOY OF PREACHING

BROOKMAN – All preachers need to study [these]...famous lectures on preaching. G

WIERSBE – ...ranks with the finest homiletical literature ever produced by any preacher of any denomination....A book every preacher ought to read once a year.... CC

Hiscox, Edward T. – PRINCIPLES AND PRACTICES FOR BAPTIST CHURCHES

BAPTIST BULLETIN – By all means get a copy of this manual. No pastor's library is complete without it. DD

BIBLICAL EVANGELIST – This book...has long been considered the classic in its field. We cannot imagine a Baptist pastor's library not containing this book, but if yours does not: get it! DD

REVIEW AND EXPOSITOR – ...a classic and a valuable resource for understanding Baptist church order, discipline and ministry. DD

MASTERS – ...the only handbook of its kind. ...it teems with definitions and is complete with résumé of Baptist history.... Every pastor should have one. O

Westing, Harold J. – MULTIPLE CHURCH-STAFF HAND-BOOK

BARBER – ...an in-depth, practical, sagacious handbook. ...his material can be applied to churches of all sizes. c

DONALD L. BUBNA – ...excellent help for developing a multiple staff. Readers will get handles on goal setting, role clarification, conducting staff meetings and leadership retreats.... Pastors will find this volume very helpful in getting started right with their team. DD

KENNETH O. GANGEL – Surpasses all other major texts on multiple church-staff ministry and should become the new standard. DD

DEVOTIONAL / CHRISTIAN LIFE

Bonar, Horatius – WHEN GOD'S CHILDREN SUFFER

GRIER – Written primarily for members of God's family under the chastening rod. L

GEORGE SWEETING – ... is an important book to help us understand human suffering. DD

Bunyan, John – THE PILGRIM'S PROGRESS

BARBER – A vivid allegory describing the experiences of a soul from the time when he is first awakened to his need of Christ until he reaches the heavenly city at the end of his earthly pilgrimage. First published in 1678. B

PAUL BECHTEL (as quoted by Merchant) – A book that both children and adults have loved for some three hundred years. Every Christian ought to read this book often. R

BROOKMAN – A classic allegory of the Christian life by an excellent devotional writer. G

CUSTER – The greatest Christian classic, second only to the Bible itself. Spurgeon read it a hundred times; Alexander Whyte preached and later published a famous series of sermons on Bunyan's characters. No preacher should be ignorant of this masterpiece. I

GRIER – [This] masterpiece by Bunyan should be in every home. L

DONALD T. KAUFFMAN – Anyone who tastes of the Pilgrim's experiences...will find here tremendous substance for meditation and clear light for all kinds of situations. DD

WIERSBE – ...it stands next to the Bible as an all-time religious best-seller and has been translated into scores of languages. ...Read it leisurely, with your heart and mind wide open. Let the book become spiritual medicine to your soul. CC

Fénelon, Francois de Salignac de la Moth – SPIRITUAL LETTERS TO WOMEN

ELISABETH ELLIOT – Fénelon...needs to be recalled in a time of supreme self-seeking, self-expression, self-indulgence and self-analysis. His example of utter submission to authority needs to be studied.... His call to simplicity needs to be heard.... DD

Havergal, Frances Ridley – KEPT FOR THE MASTER'S USE

WILLIAM J. PETERSON – Taking the words of her beloved hymn, "Take my life and let it be," the author shows what they truly mean to every Christian... DD

Henry, Matthew – THE SECRET OF COMMUNION WITH GOD

BARBER – Writes about maintaining unbroken fellowship with the Lord throughout the day. Simple and practical, and based solidly on the Word. B

PAUL BECHTEL (as quoted by Merchant) – The famous Bible commentator writes about the secret of beginning, continuing, and ending each day with God. R

MASTERS – ...[includes] many valuable pieces of counsel. Q

SHERWOOD WIRT – Matthew Henry was not a theoretician of the devotional life...he took a practical position on the Christian's daily walk with God.... I am honored to commend this treasure from the past to men and women everywhere who are seeking to investigate and understand the "mystery of serious godliness." DD

à Kempis, Thomas – IMITATION OF CHRIST

BARBER – ...first published in 1441. ...he explores the nature of spirituality with clarity, and he writes of the beauty of Christ's life with enriching simplicity. B

BECHTEL (as quoted by Merchant) – Issued in thousands of editions and translated into hundreds of languages, no book of devotion has been so widely read as this one since its appearance in 1441. Although a' Kempis tends to be a bit ascetic, he is a profound explorer of the inner life and writes with beautiful simplicity. R

WILLIAM J. PETERSON – Few books have found such universal acceptance.... [It] has become the part of the lives of millions who refer to it constantly for guidance, consolation, spiritual strength and inspiration. DD

MacLaren, Alexander – VICTORY IN FAILURE

WIERSBE – ...MacLaren has left us a wealth of sermonic material that can enrich us for eternity. You will find your own spiritual life challenged and strengthened.... DD

Meyer, F. B. – THE GIFT OF SUFFERING

MERRILL WOMACH – I believe it is one of the greatest books ever written on the subject of "why Christians suffer." DD

Murray, Andrew – ABIDE IN CHRIST

BARBER – A deeply devotional study. B

BROOKMAN – An excellent devotional study from a great writer on the Christian life. G

CUSTER – Warm-hearted meditations on living in fellowship with the Son of God, based on John 15:1-12 and other suitable passages. I

WILLIAM J. PETERSON – ...one of the first books [Andrew Murray] wrote... . ...there are 31 short chapters so you can read them one a day for a month. This will give you time to meditate. DD

Newton, John – OUT OF THE DEPTHS

GRIER – 14 autobiographical letters showing God's amazing grace, followed by a further account of Newton's life. Abridged from the original. L

HERBERT LOCKYER – ...this remarkable Christian classic, in its new dress, has come to the kingdom for such as time as this. ...we certainly need a spiritual magnet to draw us up out of the depths of sin, fear, depression and rumors of war; the reissue of Newton's soul-stirring volume provides such a magnet. N, DD

Sheldon, Charles H. – IN HIS STEPS

DONALD T. KAUFFMAN – Perhaps this book should be prefaced with a warning. Reading it may revolutionize your life....The book is actually a shocker. You will feel the shock after you have finished the last page. DD

DAVID AND KAREN MAINS – The story turns on the response of key church members to the challenge of their minister, Rev. Henry Maxwell. He requests that they join him in pledge that for one year they will make no major decisions without first asking "What would Jesus do?" Through this simple yet profound challenge, the life of Christ is manifested through individuals in this story in amazing ways. DD

Stalker, James – THE EXAMPLE OF JESUS CHRIST

BROOKMAN – ...an excellent work. G

EVERETT F. HARRISON – Reading Stalker brings both pleasure and profit. From time to time the reader encounters a compelling observation about Christ that leads him to say to himself, "Why didn't I think of that?" Let those scattered observations serve as stepping stones into the edifice itself that Stalker has built for us. DD

Stalker, James – LIVING THE CHRIST LIFE

MALCOLM CRONK – Stalker reveals insights that are timeless and expresses them in a way to be readily grasped and remembered. ...Such reading is bound to be richly instructive and inspiring. DD

Tileston, Mary W. (comp.) – GREAT SOULS AT PRAYER
DAILY STRENGTH FOR DAILY NEEDS

WILLIAM J. PETERSON – I highly recommend them. And one of the easiest and most enjoyable ways of establishing such a habit is to begin with [these books]. DD

Wagner, Charles U. – WINNING WORDS FOR DAILY LIVING

MEL JOHNSON (YOUNG WORLD RADIO) – I maintain it is one of the best devotional books ever written or printed. DD

WIERSBE – ....There is a great deal of solid spiritual nourishment in these pages, so expect to be fed....This is one devotional book that is balanced; and if we use it properly, it can help us become balanced believers who will "mount up with wings as eagles" and live in the strength of the Lord. DD

THE GODHEAD

Bickersteth, Edward H. – THE TRINITY

BAPTIST EXAMINER – ...a veritable gold mine of inspiration and information relative to the trinity.... No one could even doubt nor question the teachings of the Scriptures as to the trinity after using this book. DD

BARBER – Deals with the biblical evidence for belief in the one eternal Godhead of the Father, Son and Holy Spirit. An important contribution. B, DD

BROOKMAN – ...it is one of the most valuable treatments ever published on the Trinity. Conservative. G

CHRISTIANITY TODAY – ...should be required reading for all theological students, and would well serve as a refresher course in Christology for pastors.... DD

MASTERS – Bickersteth's unique treatment of the Trinity, complete with proof-texts; parallel column presentation of the persons of the Godhead, and extensive references. There is nothing quite like it. O

WALTER L. WILSON – There is no book like it in our language.... As you read the marvellous unfolding of the personality of these great Three, you will be led to worship God as you never did before. This book is a tonic to the soul. It is the only book...that describes in detail each of the persons of the Trinity. It presents in parallel columns the marvellous deity of each one. This book has no competition. DD

Jukes, Andrew – NAMES OF GOD

BARBER – ...these devotional studies center in the Old Testament...edifying to read. B

MASTERS – The most famous work on the names of God. The significance of Jehovah, El Shaddai, etc., is here brought out as the Divine names of both testaments are expounded. A very wordy book, but the intrepid reader will appreciate the strikingly original thought which Jukes never fails to produce. O

Wood, Nathan R. – THE TRINITY IN THE UNIVERSE

G. CAMPBELL MORGAN – ...startling, challenging, scholarly, sane, courteous.... Will surely make men stop, look and listen. DD

HISTORICAL NOVELS

Maier, Paul L. – THE FLAMES OF ROME

CHRISTIAN HERALD – A soul-shaking documentary novel of the time when society was at its worst and Christians were at their best. DD

MOODY MONTHLY – Combines secular and biblical history in a gripping account. The author is a skilled craftsman, who superbly recreates Rome under Nero. DD

CHRISTIANITY TODAY – Fascinating and impressive...eye opening...well documented. DD

Maier, Paul L. – PONTIUS PILATE

CHRISTIANITY TODAY – A magnificent job...tremendously rewarding reading. DD

CHRISTIAN HERALD – In drama, romance, color, scope and depth, this novel is comparable only to...Ben Hur, The Silver Chalice, The Robe. DD

HISTORY

Josephus, Flavius – COMPLETE WORKS OF JOSEPHUS (Whiston translation)

BARBER – A classic! Valuable as a guide to the study of the Old Testament, and helpful in understanding the history of the Jewish people.... This classic should be in every Christian's library. B, C

BROOKMAN – A complete, accurate documentation of Jewish history. It contains the first known reference to Jesus Christ by a secular historian. A classic for understanding Jewish culture and thinking. G

WILLIAM SANFORD LASOR – The best complete English translation of Josephus. DD

Maier, Paul L. – JOSEPHUS: The Essential Writings (*Jewish Antiquities* and *The Jewish War,* edited and condensed)

THE BANNER – ...the book reads as easily as the morning newspaper. My problem is that once started I couldn't lay it down...and there are 400 pages. Church librarians should have this new translation of *Josephus.* DD

BAPTIST EXAMINER – ...most helpful for those who feel they do not have time to read the complete works of Josephus. This is a new translation. It is faithful to the text by Josephus and is very readable. Paul Maier is an authority on Josephus. DD

F. F. Bruce – Dr. Maier is an authority on Josephus and on first century Christianity.... I am delighted to welcome this abridged edition which preserves the essential Josephus. I commend it warmly to all fellow students of the New Testament. DD

Christian Observer – Those concerned with the Bible and its historical context should read the works of Josephus, and those who do should strongly consider this excellent attempt at popularization. DD

Carl B. Hoch, Jr. – This new work will fill a significant need for those who have found the Elizabethan English and fine print of the Whiston edition intolerable and the astronomical price of the Loeb edition unaffordable.... Not only is this volume a very readable retranslation into modern English of the text of Josephus, but it is also an edited edition which removes (successfully in the reviewer's opinion) material which is extraneous to a free-flowing narrative and to the use of Josephus for Jewish and Christian backgrounds.... Dr. Maier is well-qualified to produce a volume of this type. I commend his new work to all readers highly. DD

Michigan Lutheran – [This] new book preserves the central thrust of Josephus' narrative and provides the historical detail essential to scholars. It reads as easily as a novel and should appeal to general readers looking for a fresh view of Old and New Testament times. DD

The Messenger – ...a very readable translation....This volume should find its way into every minister's library. DD

Prarie Overcomer – ...a very readable translation. DD

Prokope (Back to the Bible Broadcast) – This volume is a must for every pastor who wants to read Josephus for himself. DD

Sentry Magazine – I have never enjoyed *Josephus'* writings until now! This book is easy to follow, condensed, and treats the spurious comments about Jesus Christ very well. I have gladly added this book to the history section of my library. I considered this book very worthwhile. DD

Teaching Home – ...a remarkable new translation and condensation....You and your children can sit down with this book and read it almost as if it were a novel which it is—a novel way to increase your understanding of the vital events up to and after the time of Christ. DD

THE HOLY SPIRIT

Baxter, Ronald E. – GIFTS OF THE SPIRIT

John F. Walvoord (In *Bibliotheca Sacra*) – Readers will find this a helpful, understandable, and carefully thought-through presentation of the gifts of the Spirit, so essential for effective Christian service. DD

Voices – Exploding the myths surrounding the subject, Baxter presents a meticulous, rewarding study of the biblical teaching on spiritual gifts. DD

Bickersteth, Edward H. – THE HOLY SPIRIT

BARBER – A complete study of the personality of the Godhead and the divine work of the Holy Spirit. B

UNITED EVANGELICAL – This is a very valuable contribution to our enlightenment of the Holy Spirit's ministry. It is scholarly, yet understandable by laymen. DD

Biederwolf, William Edward – STUDY OF THE HOLY SPIRIT

BARBER – ...this brief, conservative study covers the important aspects of the Paraclete's person and work. C

MASTERS – ...as positive and humble as its title. [Biederwolf] gives the student his "homework" already done, assembling all the references to the Holy Spirit: baptism, filling, etc. Highly recommended as the finest work of its kind. Has outstanding chapters on the Sealing, Anointing, Communion, Baptism and Filling of the Spirit. O

Bullinger, E. W. – WORD STUDIES ON THE HOLY SPIRIT

BARBER – Bullinger provides a penetrating study of the biblical teaching. Ultradispensational. C

WIERSBE – ...unique in that it is both a concordance and a concise commentary on every verse in the New Testament that uses the word "spirit" (*pneuma*). One of the older works that had a steady ministry and is sure to last. DD

Gardiner, George E. – THE CORINTHIAN CATASTROPHE

OHIO INDEPENDENT BAPTIST – ...clearly answers the arguments proposed by today's charismatic adherents. It would be well for pastors to make this easily understood book available to their people. DD

W. WILBERT WELCH – ...Gardiner has put his finger on the Corinthian problem. In a very splendid way he answers the matter of the Corinthians seeking and displaying the showy gifts. DD

Koch, Kurt E. – SPEAKING IN TONGUES?

BARBER – Provides the author's closely reasoned evaluation of the biblical teaching on tongues, summarizes the teaching of leaders in the history of the Christian church, carefully sifts the evidence of "case histories," and provides the author's statement of the "biblical counterpart." B

CONCORDIA – A helpful contribution to the writings on the "tongues" movement. DD

COVENANTER WITNESS – ...a stimulating analysis of the "modern tongues movement" .... It is well worth the few minutes it takes to be read. DD

Marsh, F. E. – EMBLEMS OF THE HOLY SPIRIT

BAPTIST BIBLE TRIBUNE – Most practical and lucid discussion of the subjects we have been privileged to read. DD

BIBLIOTHECA SACRA – Sane in the interpretation of symbols, and warmly devotional and heart-warming in the application of the truth concerning the scriptural teaching on the Holy Spirit's work. DD

CHRISTIANITY TODAY – The detailed explanations of the symbols of the Holy Spirit...are done with a freshness and originality seldom excelled, plus sound exegesis. DD

JOHN F. WALVOORD (as quoted by Merchant) – ...[an] important...study of the many figures in the Bible speaking of the Holy Spirit. Q

GEORGE WILLIAMS – Excellent little book. DD

Morgan, James – THE BIBLICAL DOCTRINE OF THE HOLY SPIRIT

EVANGELICAL CHRISTIAN (as quoted by Barber) – Controversy and criticism are avoided. Scripture ideas are unfolded in a clear and popular way, so as not only to inform the judgment, but also to purify the heart. C

Owen, John – THE HOLY SPIRIT

BARBER – One of the outstanding books of all time. Presents a learned and spiritual analysis of the names and titles of the Spirit, His nature and personality, and His varied works and influence. B

BROOKMAN – An outstanding one-volume study on the person and work of the Holy Spirit. This extensive work contains 356 pages. G

GRIER – ...[it] should not be neglected.... L

MASTERS – Another completely successful condensation of a renowned classic...the whole of Owen's reasoning on the Holy Spirit in one magnificent volume. O

JOHN F. WALVOORD (as quoted by Merchant) – ...a theological classic, this work is one of the most thorough treatments of the subject.... R

Schwab, Richard C. – LET THE BIBLE SPEAK...ABOUT TONGUES

JOSEPH C. ALDRICH – A thorough treatment of the tongues issue.... DD

EARL D. RADMACHER – ...the finest balance of careful scholarship and practical application that I have seen on the subject. If I were to pick one book to give to a person to read [about tongues] that is THE book. DD, C

JOHN F. WALVOORD – True to the Scriptures...should be helpful to Christians seeking biblical answers to this important subject. DD

Thomas, W. H. Griffith – THE HOLY SPIRIT

BARBER – [These lectures] have won the admiration of theologians in all parts of the English-speaking world. [They] survey the work of the Spirit in biblical revelation, historical interpretation, theological formulation, and modern application. B

PACKER – The author's clear, crisp, straightforward style, joined as it is with wisdom, both theological and devotional, gives his expository works classic status. DD

SUGDEN – All [Griffith Thomas'] writings bear the stamp of heaven and true greatness on them. His zenith of Bible exposition is certainly reached in this work! Each of the thirty-two chapters is like an "…apple of gold in a picture of silver." DD, Z

WIERSBE – Griffith Thomas excels in spiritual depth, practicality and a simplicity of expression that make the most profound truths come alive with excitement. DD

Unger, Merrill F. – NEW TESTAMENT TEACHING ON TONGUES

BAPTIST BULLETIN – A thorough, scholarly, and biblical study…. DD

COVENANTER WITNESS – Thorough, convincing…. DD

INNER WITNESS – …a gold mine…. Thoroughly scriptural and eminently scholarly. DD

MASTERS – Typically clear and easy presentation…. O

MUSIC MINISTRY

Osbeck, Kenneth W. – 101 HYMN STORIES
101 MORE HYMN STORIES

BARBER – Osbeck['s]…handling of the material is excellent. [These two books] make delightful devotional reading. Preachers will also find that the material presented can be used to enhance the worship service. We are grateful to him for his research and for making the benefits of his study available in such a pleasing way. C

BROOKMAN – Excellent for devotional readings, sermon illustrations and bulletin inserts. G

WIERSBE – I appreciate these books…they are filled with good illustrative material about the great hymns and gospel songs so familiar to our people. DD

PRAYER

Dods, Marcus – THE PRAYER THAT TEACHES TO PRAY

CUSTER – A fervent, eloquent, and powerful exposition of the Lord's Prayer. Although the reader may not agree with everything here, he will be struck with more devotional inspirational thoughts per page than he would think possible. I

MILLIE DIENERT – When you finish these pages, I'm sure you will agree with me that valuable lessons have been gleaned from them. For every Christian this book is a necessary reading and for every teacher and preacher, it's a must! DD

Rainsford, Marcus – OUR LORD PRAYS FOR HIS OWN: Thoughts on John 17

BARBER – Timely, relevant, devotional thoughts on John 17. ...the greatest classic ever written on Christ's high priestly prayer.... B, C

BROOKMAN – These extensive studies on John 17 are timely, relevant and devotional. This work is considered to be one of the greatest classics ever written on Christ's high priestly prayer. G

JOHN W. CAWOOD (as quoted in Jones) – ...it makes one bow in awe to Christ. It is a rare book, worth reading more than once. M

CUSTER – Powerful devotional messages on every verse of John 17. I

MASTERS – ...an exceedingly warm treatment of John 17.... These pages teem with what used to be called elevated spiritual thought. As a spiritual refresher it is magnificent and is a source of stimulation for preachers with so much original material. It expounds evangelical unity in a totally spiritual rather than organizational manner.... P

SMITH – ...one of the great devotional classics of our language. There are many volumes on this exceptionally rich chapter from the fourth Gospel, but none can begin to compare with the one by Rainsford. Occasionally I have given copies of this book to friends, and I have never failed to have them say to me that it is the greatest devotional volume they have ever had in their hands. This book will lead one to the throne of grace; it is a book to place at the bedside to read for the refreshing of one's soul late at night or early morning. Words fail to describe the wealth these pages will convey. U

W. H. GRIFFITH THOMAS – ...Deals with the "Holy of Holies" of our Lord's earthly life, and those who prayerfully read it through, Bible in hand, will find ample reward in its exposition of doctrine and its application of truth to mind and heart. DD

WIERSBE – ...obtain this work. BB

Saphir, Adolph – OUR LORD'S PATTERN FOR PRAYER

BARBER – Fervent messages that expound the text and edify the reader. Frequent digressions into matters of theological importance make fascinating reading. ...a must for every believer. B, C

BROOKMAN – This classic reprint is a thorough work on "The Lord's Prayer." It will be difficult to find a more complete and exegetical book than Saphir on this important study. Each section is systematically outlined for ease of understanding. Practical. G

WIERSBE – ...one of the best on [this] very special portion of Scripture. Saphir...blends pastoral warmth with good exegesis. ...I especially appreciate the insights he gives from Jewish lore and custom. Best of all, Saphir magnifies the person of our Lord Jesus Christ, so that the reading of this book is almost an experience of worship. DD

Scroggie, W. Graham – HOW TO PRAY

BARBER – Deals effectively with such topics as adoration, confession, petition, intercession, and thanksgiving. C

Scroggie, W. Graham – PAUL'S PRISON PRAYERS

WIERSBE – Valuable.... How that man could preach and teach the Word of God! DD

PROPHECY

Anderson, Sir Robert – FORGOTTEN TRUTHS

BAPTIST MESSENGER – ...cherished truths, brought to focus. DD

BARBER – Insightful. C

CALVARY REVIEW – We are indebted to the late Robert Anderson for his great classic.... DD

Andrews, Samuel J. – CHRISTIANITY AND ANTI-CHRISTIANITY IN THEIR FINAL CONFLICT

BARBER – Highly acclaimed, yet long out-of-print, this work deserves to be studied by every professing Bible student. C

BROOKMAN – A great work on the study of the Antichrist and the apostasy of the last days. G

JAMES M. GRAY (quoted by Wilbur M. Smith) – "...Here are no wild fancies, no foolish setting of times and seasons, no crude and sensational interpretations of prophecy, but a calm setting forth of what the Bible says on the most important subject for these times." U

Baron, David – ISRAEL IN THE PLAN OF GOD

BROOKMAN – This book deals with the four major passages of Scripture that deal exclusively with Israel's history. G

LIBRARIAN'S WORLD – ...an excellent commentary; challenging, scholarly, and directed toward the more serious Bible student. DD

PULPIT HELPS – The reader will not want to miss any of the inspiring details of this exposition. DD

JOHN F. WALVOORD – ...will contribute much insight. DD

Blackstone, William E. (W.E.B.) – JESUS IS COMING

ARNETT – ...a classic presentation concerning the personal, premillennial coming of Jesus Christ....The most widely circulated book on the subject with a correspondingly great influence. R

BROOKMAN – A classic work on the return of Jesus Christ. Blackstone packs a lot of helpful information into this volume. Premillennial. G

SPURGEON – Masterpiece of extraordinary learning and critical skill.... DD

R. A. TORREY – ...one of the books that has had a decidedly formative influence on my life and teaching. I have always recommended it to those who are beginning the study of the subject. DD

JOHN F. WALVOORD – Everyone interested in prophecy should read this [book].... DD

Bultema, Harry – MARANATHA! A Study of Unfulfilled Prophecies

BARBER – ...this is an important treatise, which Bible students of all persuasions will appreciate. c

BIBLIOTHECA SACRA – This is a very important document for anyone interested in the premillennial interpretation of Scripture. Readers will find it a mine of information.... The author has done an exceedingly careful piece of work that deserves study by those who wish to be informed in this area of doctrine. DD

Peters, George N. H. – THE THEOCRATIC KINGDOM (3 vols.)

BARBER – ...ranks as one of the greatest studies on the interpretation of the prophetic word ever produced. Discourses at length on the theocratic kingdom concept contained in the Scriptures. Sometimes laborious, but no one can claim to have a thorough grasp of this subject until he has interacted with this treatise. Indispensable and highly recommended. Espouses a midtribulation rapture. B

BROOKMAN – A truly monumental work on the study of Bible prophecy. This work is a classic.... Highly recommended by Wilbur M. Smith. Premillennial. G

LEWIS SPERRY CHAFER (quoted in *Prairie Overcomer*] – ...the greatest work on prophetic interpretation ever written.... DD

MOO – A classic of historic premillennial theology. R

DWIGHT D. PENTECOST – ...the most exhaustive, scholarly, reverent treatment of the questions of the kingdom of our Lord available today.. DD

SMITH – ...this [is] without question the greatest work on the Second Advent of our Lord Jesus and the many subjects relating to the Second Advent, ever published in our language. ...there is no work in the English language that deals with this...important subject with such depth, clearness, and understanding.... What a tragedy that a vast amount of learning like this should be hardly known to the Christian world within half a century after it is published! U

Pink, Arthur – THE ANTICHRIST

BARBER – A very capable synthesis of the biblical evidence surrounding the person and work of the Antichrist. A work of exceptional merit. B

BIBLICAL EVANGELIST – ...one of the most thorough studies of this theme written in the twentieth century. DD

Powell, Ivor – WHAT IN THE WORLD WILL HAPPEN NEXT?

BAPTIST BULLETIN – You will be challenged by this fine presentation of biblical prophecy. DD

CHRISTIAN BOOKSELLER – ...written with an uncommon humbleness not normally found in books written about prophecy. A text for both pastor and student of prophecy. DD

PROPHETIC WITNESS – A readable and worthwhile book. DD

WIERSBE – Don't overlook [this] book.... [It is] filled with treasures of sermon ideas and spiritual truths to help you in your ministry. DD

SALVATION

Anderson, Sir Robert – THE GOSPEL AND ITS MINISTRY

BARBER – A complete survey of Bible doctrine. Contains a clear definition of terms, with excellent illustrations. Ideal for Bible study groups. B

Anderson, Sir Robert – REDEMPTION TRUTHS

BARBER – ...show[s], as well as man can, the marvels of God's plan for our redemption. Well done; stimulating. C

Denney, James – BIBLICAL DOCTRINE OF RECONCI-LIATION

BARBER (quoting Alexander Whyte) – "Read it again and again, and then preach its doctrine all your days...I do not know any modern book that has so much preaching power in it." Well conceived and executed. B, C

BROOKMAN – Most all of Denny's works are of the utmost value. G

Westcott, Frederick Brooke – THE BIBLICAL DOCTRINE OF JUSTIFICATION

BROOKMAN – An important work that is based upon Paul's Roman and Galatian letters. This volume is thorough in exegesis. G

SCIENCE

Pember, G. H. – EARTH'S EARLIEST AGES

BAPTIST BULLETIN – Most revealing study of an oft-neglected subject. DD

G. H. LANG – It is with every confidence that I commend to my fellow-servants of Christ this illuminating treatise. I know of none other on its theme to be compared with it in spiritual value. DD

INNER WITNESS – Its pages burn with revealing truth and illumination...you need a copy in your library for reading and reference. DD

PROPHETIC WITNESS – ...extremely valuable to the Bible student. DD

SERMONS, OUTLINES AND ILLUSTRATIONS

Evans, Christmas – SERMONS AND MEMOIRS OF CHRISTMAS EVANS

BAPTIST BULLETIN – This volume is well worth reading by pastors, teachers and lay folk everywhere. DD

BEREA BANNER – You have never heard good preaching until you have read these sermons.... Buy, beg, borrow, but obtain this book. You will never be the same after you read it! DD

BIBLICAL EVANGELIST – We warmly recommend this good volume! DD

BRITISH COLUMBIA FELLOWSHIP BAPTIST MESSENGER – These books will feed the soul and encourage the heart as they are fully digested. DD

WIERSBE – These sermons will be a turning point for many in their ministry of preaching. I rejoice that this rare volume is back in print. You will not be the same after reading this book. DD

Finney, Charles G. – Finney Memorial Library
GOD'S LOVE FOR A SINNING WORLD
GUILT OF SIN
PREVAILING PRAYER
SO GREAT SALVATION
TRUE AND FALSE REPENTANCE
TRUE SAINTS
TRUE SUBMISSION
VICTORY OVER THE WORLD

BAPTIST BIBLE – ...well organized, logical, and practical. DD

BARBER – A collection of sermons by a great revival preacher. These messages speak to the conditions within the church, and also relate to the world in general. B

CALVARY REVIEW – ...hard-hitting messages.... It will be impossible for the reader to avoid self-evaluation and examination. DD

Fuller, David Otis (ed.) – SPURGEON'S SERMON NOTES: Genesis to Revelation

JOWETT – An inexhaustive mine of thought and suggestion. DD

BRITISH WEEKLY – ...A running commentary on the New Testament...the best of the great preacher. DD

Lockyer, Herbert – LAST WORDS OF SAINTS AND SINNERS

BARBER – Recounts the testimonies of those whose simple faith in Christ was sufficient for the crises confronting them. Also contains the testimony of those who turned to Christ in their final hours. Provides source material and illustrations for sermons. B

BROOKMAN – Lockyer is an extremely practical writer on many subjects. This work provides helpful resource material in sermon preparation. G

Powell, Ivor – Outlines and Illustrations
BIBLE CAMEOS
BIBLE GEMS

BIBLE HIGHWAYS
BIBLE NAMES OF CHRIST
BIBLE PINNACLES
BIBLE TREASURES
BIBLE WINDOWS

BAPTIST BULLETIN – Concise, imaginative and stimulating.... DD

BAPTIST EXAMINER – ...brief, highly informative and suggestive studies. DD

WIERSBE – Don't overlook these fine books...they are filled with treasures of sermon ideas and spiritual truths to help you in your ministry. DD

Powell, Ivor – BIBLE NAMES OF CHRIST

AUSTRALIAN EVANGELICAL – ...contains a wealth of suggestive material for devotional use or sermon preparation. DD

BAPTIST EXAMINER – ...the author has done the busy pastor a good service in this book....one can find material that is helpful, that will bless the soul, and that can be used in sermon preparation. DD

BOOKTALK – ...More than anything, this publication will stir the heart of the believer with a glorious picture of Christ. DD

Proctor, F. B. (ed.) – TREASURY OF QUOTATIONS ON RELIGIOUS SUBJECTS

LOUIS PAUL LEHMAN – ...[a] treasure chest of centuries [which contains] the air of immortality.... A masterpiece of the classification of material.... The power and beauty of language come glistening from the pages.... Gems of thought which can run, walk, creep and sit down, as well as soar. Thoroughly Christ-centered. DD, Y

PROPHETIC NEWS AND ISRAEL'S WATCHMAN – This time-saving and practical volume will introduce minds to otherwise unattainable writings and...stimulate great thoughts.... Preachers, librarians, students, teachers, writers and speakers will save hours of labor...by keeping this welcome resource book within reach. DD

Whitesell, Faris D. – 65 WAYS TO GIVE EVANGELISTIC INVITATIONS

BARBER – Unique because it is the only work of its kind. B

PREACHING – While there are many books about the mechanics of sermon preparation, there is very little help on the mechanics of giving a public invitation.... [This]...is the most complete book in print. DD

ROBERT G. LEE – ...a most helpful book...of great worth.... Will give courage to the timid, skill to the awkward, prompting to the perplexed, help to the hesitant and effectiveness to the ineffective in the matter of giving Gospel invitations.... Deserves a wide sale and reading and practice. DD

SWORD OF THE LORD – This is an excellent little book and is written in a manner that is interesting and motivational. We recommend it. DD

Wiersbe, Warren W. (comp.) – Classic Sermons Series
CLASSIC SERMONS ON THE ATTRIBUTES OF GOD
CLASSIC SERMONS ON CHRISTIAN SERVICE
CLASSIC SERMONS ON THE CROSS OF CHRIST
CLASSIC SERMONS ON FAITH AND DOUBT
CLASSIC SERMONS ON PRAYER
CLASSIC SERMONS ON THE PRODIGAL SON
CLASSIC SERMONS ON THE RESURRECTION
CLASSIC SERMONS ON SUFFERING
CLASSIC SERMONS ON WORSHIP

BAPTIST BULLETIN – These selected messages...will quicken your thinking, stir your emotions, and mover your sluggish will. DD

BARBER – Recommended. C

CLERGY JOURNAL – ...a must for all clergy. It will provide some answers for use in sermons and in counseling. DD

PREACHING MAGAZINE – Warren Wiersbe enthusiasm for the pulpit is evident in his several collections of sermons from great preachers....Each provides an example of serious doctrinal preaching--and of effective communication of theological truth. DD

PROPHETIC WITNESS – ...will enrich and bless the reader. DD

SWORD OF THE LORD – ...they will greatly bless the hearts of those who read them. We recommend the book. DD

Wiersbe, Warren W. (comp.) – TREASURY OF THE WORLD'S GREAT SERMONS

BROOKMAN – ...helpful collection of 122 outstanding sermons from 122 of the greatest preachers with a short biographical description of each preacher. Excellent. G

CHRISTIAN REVIEW – ...a sermon library in one volume.... DD

EMPHASIS MAGAZINE – A rewarding volume. DD

EVANGELICAL BAPTIST – ...a worthwhile gift for a pastor or a young person training for the ministry. DD

INTEREST – ...a great volume to put into the hands of young preachers—an ideal gift! DD

PULPIT HELPS – It's doubtful if any preacher can fail to benefit from the reading and study of such a treasury as this. DD

SPIRIT BEINGS

Koch, Kurt E. – BETWEEN CHRIST AND SATAN

KING'S BUSINESS – This is not a book for the novice or the careless Christian, but could be a profitable experience for the pastor and Christian worker who is ready to face some of the deeper problems of Christian personality and satanic forces. DD

UNITED EVANGELICAL ACTION – An unusual portrayal of spiritism, fortune telling, magic and other fields of psychic subjection illustrated with various first-hand examples and case studies.

Koch, Kurt E. – CHRISTIAN COUNSELING AND OCCULTISM

BARBER (IN PSYCHOLOGY FOR LIVING) – One of the finest in-depth works of its kind. DD

LAWERENCE J. CRABB, JR. – The definitive work in this area. DD

LUTHERN ALERT – ...a practical, theological and systematic investigation in the light of present day psychological and medical knowledge. DD

PRARIE OVERCOMER – ...a valuable treatment of a subject largely ignored by fundamental christians. DD

Koch, Kurt E. – DEMONOLOGY, PAST AND PRESENT

BAPTIST RECORD – The messages are clear in outline and present a broad scholarly analysis and interpretation. DD

PRESBYTERIAN JOURNAL – ...valuable to the serious Christian as well as the pastor who is daily confronted with problems from the lives of people who have experemented with many or any kind of occult exercises. DD

Koch, Kurt E. – THE DEVIL'S ALPHABET

ALLIANCE WITNESS – ...highly recommended for ministers, church libraries and alert Christians. DD

BARBER – A review of forty-seven forms of superstition, fortune-telling, magic, and spiritism. B

LUTHERAN ALERT – ...a handy handbook. DD

Koch, Kurt E. – OCCULT ABC

AUSTIN RECORD – ...an interesting and scholarly work, probably a very necessary work, showing the pitfalls the unwary must avoid. DD

BARBER – A must for those who work with teens and those in college. Should be in every church library. C

Koch, Kurt E. – OCCULT BONDAGE AND DELIVERANCE

C. FRED DICKASON (IN MOODY MONTHLY) – If there were one popular level book that I would recommend to every pastor and Christian counselor, this is it for understanding and helping those oppressed by the hidden things of Satan. DD

ADVANCE (GOSPEL PUBLISHING HOUSE) – ...the author identifies the many forms of occultism, spiritism, and demonic activity, describes results of becoming involved and shows the deliverance available through Christ. DD

TYPOLOGY

SEE ALSO "The Tabernacle"

Fairbairn, Patrick – TYPOLOGY OF SCRIPTURE (2 Vols. in one)

BARBER – A systematic treatment of typology...the best ever written on this subject. **B**

BROOKMAN – A classic....The most conclusive evangelical work on typology. A thorough study of the pictures of redemption and the Redeemer which God has given to us...as well as the principles for the interpretation of types. **G**

GRIER – [The] standard work on the subject....sober and most helpful. **L**

Habershon, Ada R. – STUDY OF THE TYPES

BARBER – A detailed, devotional study of the Old Testament types and their fulfillment in the New Testament. **DD**

BROOKMAN – ...full of useful hints, thoughts and illustrations.... **G**

WIERSBE – A classic treatment. **CC**

Jukes, Andrew – THE LAW OF THE OFFERINGS

BARBER – Beginning with a defense of biblical typology, the writer analyzes the five offerings of the Levitical system and discusses the typical significance of each. **B**

BROOKMAN – This work is a classic on the typological significance of the offerings mentioned in Leviticus, showing how each clearly points to some particular aspect of the redemptive work of Christ. The author clearly defines the significance of this Judeo-religious rite and its application to the New Testament church. **G**

MASTERS – No one else explains the significance of the Levitical offerings (in relation to Calvary) as well as Jukes does here.... Suddenly...it bursts into life with several superb chapters which are practically essential to the study of Leviticus. **P**

SPURGEON – A very condensed, instructive, refreshing book. It will open up new trains of thought to those unversed in the teaching of the types. **Y**

Keach, Benjamin – PREACHING FROM THE TYPES AND METAPHORS OF THE BIBLE

BROOKMAN – Every pastor will glean sermonic material from this classical reprint.... Keach gives a complete analysis of the spiritual significance of each type and metaphor along with its practical application for today. **G**

LOCKYER – ...believers throughout the Christian world should know of and revere the witness and work of Benjamin Keach. I am not ashamed to confer how deeply in debt I am to the most substantial studies of this renowned expositor. **N**

MASTERS – ...packed with rich suggestion for preachers. Those who can catch (and update) the spirit of this great preacher will derive much stimulation. o

SPURGEON – This is a vast cyclopedia of types and metaphors of all sorts, and was once very popular. It is a capital book, though too often the figures not only run on all-fours but on as many legs as a centipede. y

SOURCE CODE LIST

(All quotes taken from the following sources are used by permission.)

A. Allison, Joseph D. *Bible Study Resource Guide*, revised edition. Grand Rapids: Sagamore Books, 1984.

B. Barber, Cyril J. *The Minister's Library*, vol. 1. Chicago: Moody Press, 1985.

C. Barber, Cyril J. *The Minister's Library*, vol. 2. Chicago: Moody Press, 1985.

D. Barker, Kenneth L., Waltke, Bruce K. (comp.), Zuck, Roy B. (ed.). *Bibliography for Old Testament Exegesis and Exposition.* Dallas: Dallas Theological Seminary, 1975

E. Bollier, John A. *The Literature of Theology: A Guide for Students and Pastors.* Philadelphia: The Westminster Press, 1979.

F. Branson, Mark Lau. *The Reader's Guide to the Best Evangelical Books.* San Francisco: Harper & Row Publishers, Inc. 1982.

G. Brookman, David W. *Basic Books for the Minister's Library.* Shippensburg, PA: Destiny Image Publishers, 1986.

H. Childs, Brevard S. *Old Testament Books for Pastor and Teacher.* Philadelphia: The Westminster Press, 1977.

I. Custer, Stewart. *Tools for Preaching and Teaching the Bible.* Greenville, SC: Bob Jones University Press, Inc. 1981.

J. Danker, Frederick W. *Multipurpose Tools for Bible Study.* St. Louis: Concordia Publishing House, 1966.

K. Fair, J. Arnold. Respected Bible professor, pastor, and author.

L.   Grier, W. J. *The Best Books: A Guide to Christian Literature.* London: The Banner of Truth, 1968.

M.   Jones, Charles E., ed. *The Books You Read.* Harrisburg, PA: Executive Books, 1986.

N.   Lockyer, Herbert, Sr. Late author of many books including *Last Words of Saints and Sinners.* Grand Rapids: Kregel Publications, 1969.

O.   Martin, Ralph P. *New Testament Books for Pastor and Teacher.* Philadelphia: The Westminster Press, 1984.

P.   Masters, Peter. M.   Pastor of Metropolitan Tabernacle in London, and author of *The Preacher's Library.* London: Wakeman Publishers Ltd, 1979.

Q.   Masters, Peter. M. Pastor of Metropolitan Tabernacle in London, and author of *Survey of Bible Commentaries.* London: Metropolitan Tabernacle, 1983.

R.   Merchant, Harish, ed. *Encounter With Books: A Guide to Christian Reading.* 2nd printing, 1971. Intervarsity Press, P. O. Box 1400, Downers Grove, IL 60515.

S.   Moo, Douglas, ed. *An Annotated Bibliography on the Bible and the Church.* Deerfield, IL: Trinity Evangelical Divinity School, 1986.

T.   Packer, J. I. Respected professor and author of numerous works, including *Knowing God.*

U.   Smith, Wilbur M. *A Treasury of Books for Bible Study.* Boston: W. A. Wilde Co., 1960.

V.   Smith, Wilbur M. *Chats From a Minister's Library.* Boston: W. A. Wilde Co., 1951.

W.   Smith, Wilbur M. *Profitable Bible Study.* Boston: W. A. Wilde Co., 1951.

X.   Smith, Wilbur M. *The Minister in His Study.* Boston: W. A. Wilde Co., 1973.

Y.   Spurgeon, Charles Haddon. *Commenting and Commentaries.* Grand Rapids: Kregel Publications, 1988.

Z.   Sugden, Dr. Howard F. Respected pastor, conference speaker and author of several books, including *What Does the Bible Say About...?* Grand Rapids: Kregel Publications, 1987.

AA. Tenney, Merrill C. Respected professor and author of many works including *New Testament Survey,* and editor of *The Zondervan Pictorial Bible Encyclopedia.*

BB. Wiersbe, Warren W. *Listening to the Giants*, including "A Basic Library for Bible Students." Grand Rapids: Baker Book House, 1980.

CC. Wiersbe, Warren W. *Walking With the Giants.* Grand Rapids: Baker Book House, 1976.

DD. Recorded recommendations and printed forewords, prefaces, covers, jackets, and periodicals.

EE. Rosscup, James E. *Commentaries for Biblical Expositors*, 1983.

AUTHOR INDEX

SUBJECT INDEX

85

"A good library should be looked upon as an indispensible part of church furniture; and the deacons whose business it is to serve tables will be wise if...they give an eye to the study table and keep it supplied with new works and standard books in fair abundance."

— Charles H. Spurgeon

"The preacher must inevitably be a man of the Book and also a man of books. A good portion of his life must be committed to his library....Great preachers almost inevitably have been men who were broadly read in the great books of the world."

— Dr. D. James Kennedy,
in the foreword to
The Books You Read,
edited by Charles E. Jones

"I trust that the bringing together of these studies, chiefly relating to biblical subjects, will arouse in many ministers a desire for a more serious, constant study of the Word of God, and of the great books that have been written to help us understand these Divine oracles. And I can also hope that some things set forth here will save many from wasting money and time in the purchase and reading of those superficial works which, however glowing might be their blurbs and advertising, will fade into oblivion before a given year is past.

In these pages I am only attempting to give some guidance to those who want to read, and who know they should read, but who are bewildered by the large number of books they observe in the bookstores or see advertised in religious journals. Even the Apostle Paul, author of the most profound treatises the Church will ever know, after all those wonderful years of evangelism, in the last days of his life on earth, knowing that at any time he might be called out of the Mamertine Prison to lay down his life for Christ, asked Timothy to bring "the books and the parchments." He never lost his love for reading, and no doubt he never had the time for reading all that he longed to read."

— Wilbur M. Smith,
in *Treasury of Books*

"If religious books are not widely circulated among the masses in this country, I do not know what is going to become of us as a nation. If truth be not diffused, error will be; if God and His Word are not known and received, the devil and his works will gain ascendancy; if the evangelical volume does not reach every hamlet, the pages of a corrupt and licentious literature will; if the power of the Gospel is not felt throughout the length and breadth of the land, anarchy and misrule, degradation and misery, corruption and darkness, will reign without mitigation or end."

— Daniel Webster

"While you have a world of books on a thousand subjects to choose from, live in **the** Book of the World, for if God has called you to preach, he expects you to be a specialist in such a supreme Book as you can be, by the constant illumination of Him who gave such a Book to the world."

—Herbert W. Lockyer, Sr.

"You are the same today as you will be in five years except for two things, the people you meet and the books you read."   —Charles E. (Tremendous) Jones

"The ministry of books can be used to evangelize, teach, train, and expel ignorance as it has done in the past. A cursory glance at history should convince us that God has used books and literature to enlighten blinded peoples and nations."

"Have we forgotten that Christianity is primarily a religion of facts—historical facts? The Bible is a body of divine information; and to be ignorant of the information is to be ignorant of Christianity and to be ignorant of God."

"The printed page never flinches, it never shows cowardice; it is never tempted to compromise. The printed page never gets tired; it never gets disheartened. The printed page travels cheaply—you can be a missionary for the price of a stamp. It requires no buildings in which to operate. The printed page works while you sleep. It never loses its temper in discussion. And it works when you are gone from the scene. The printed page is a visitor that gets inside the home and stays there. It always catches a man in the right mood, it speaks to him only when he is reading it. It never answers back and it sticks to the point."

"Every great book is an action, and every great action is a book."   —Martin Luther

"No other agency can penetrate so deeply, witness so daringly, abide so persistently and influence so irresistibly as the printed page." —Samuel Zwemer, *Missionary Statesman*

"A minister can lead his people to see the importance of the use of good literature just as he leads them in other truths"

"In the past the pen has been the hammer to break the errors of centuries. But now the enemies of the truth have learned the value of books and with word processors and printing presses they have left those who love the biblical Christianity far behind."

"A book by Richard Sibbes, one of the choicest of the Puritan writers, was read by Richard Baxter, who was greatly blessed by it. Baxter then wrote his *Call To The Unconverted* which deeply influenced Philip Doddridge, who in turn wrote *The Rise and Progress of Religion in the Soul*. This brought the young William Wilberforce, subsequent English statesman and foe of slavery, to serious thoughts of eternity. Wilberforce wrote his *Practical Book of Christianity* which fired the soul of Leigh Richmond. Richmond, in turn, wrote *The Dairyman's Daughter*, a book that brought thousands to the Lord, helping Thomas Chalmers the great preacher, among others."

"A drop of ink may make a million think." —Byron

"God be thankful for books. They are voices of the distant and the dead, and make us heirs of the spiritual life of past ages."
—Channing

". . . all that mankind has done, thought, gained or been: it is lying as in magic preservation in the pages of books. They are the chosen possessions of men."
—Carlyle

"A blessed companion is a book–a book that, fitly chosen, is a lifelong friend, . . . a book that, at a touch, pours its heart into our own."
—Douglas Jerrold

"Many times the reading of a book has made the future of man."
—Emerson

"When is human nature so weak as in the bookstore?"
—Henry Ward Beecher

"A good book on your shelf is a friend that turns its back on you and remains a friend."
—Ross Macdonald

"If a man can purchase but very few books, my first advice to him would be, let him purchase the very best. If he cannot spend much, let him spend well."
—Charles Haddon Spurgeon

"A library is a true fairyland, a vary palace of delight, a haven of repose from the storms and troubles of the world. Rich and poor can enjoy it alike, for here at least, wealth gives no advantage."
—Avebury

"A smallest tract may be the stone in David's sling. In the hands of Christ, it may bring down a giant soul."
—Robert Murray McCheyne

". . . a good book is the precious life-blood of a master spirit."
—John Milton

"Be careful what book you read, for as water tastes of the soul it runs through, so does the soul taste of the authors that a man reads."
—John Trapp

"If I could control the literature of the household, I could guarantee the well-being of the church and state."
—Francis Bacon

"We must throw the printer's inkpot at the devil!"
—Martin Luther

"The books which help you most are those which make you think the most. The hardest way of learning is by easy reading: but a great book that comes from a great thinker — it is a ship of thought, deep freighted with truth and with beauty.
—Theodore Parker

"The first time I read an excellent book, it is to me just as if I had gained a new friend. When I read over a book I have perused before, it resembles the meeting with an old one.
—Oliver Goldsmith

Helping you build a better understanding of the best in Christian literature is what *A Classic Bible Study Library for Today* is all about! Additional comments on over 1,400 Bible commentaries can be found in:

Commenting and Commentaries

by
Charles H. Spurgeon

Spurgeon provides a classic introduction to preaching and the use of commentaries, as well as helpful, pithy, and oftentimes humorous comments on these titles. While some of the books are out of print and available only through secondhand bookstores, many have since been reprinted. All entries have been updated to show the current publishers; the text has been completely reset for easier reading and reference; and an index of authors and titles has been added.

Whether you are a pastor, student or layperson, *Commenting and Commentaries* will be a valuable resource, both in your ministry and as you select Bible commentaries for your library.

Trade Paper, 288 pp.

ISBN 0-8254-3749-0

Available from Christian booktores, or:

KREGEL *Publications*

P. O. Box 2607 • Grand Rapids, MI 49501-2607